MAC

PHILIP

L. A. Movie

MACMILLAN

MACMILLAN READERS

UPPER LEVEL

Founding Editor: John Milne

The Macmillan Readers provide a choice of enjoyable reading materials for learners of English. The series is published at six levels – Starter, Beginner, Elementary, Pre-intermediate, Intermediate and Upper.

Level control

Information, structure and vocabulary are controlled to suit the students' ability at each level.

The number of words at each level:

Starter	about 300 basic words
Beginner	about 600 basic words
Elementary	about 1100 basic words
Pre-intermediate	about 1400 basic words
Intermediate	about 1600 basic words
Upper	about 2200 basic words

Vocabulary

Some difficult words and phrases in this book are important for understanding the story. Some of these words are explained in the story and some are shown in the pictures. From Pre-intermediate level upwards, words are marked with a number like this: …[3]. These words are explained in the Glossary at the end of the book.

Contents

The People in This Story

Josie

Julie Grant

Steve Tovich

Arabella Annie

Vincent Calab

Theo Z. Democrates

Detective Dickinson

Captain Roberto Garcia

Sergeant Kamal

1

The Purple Palace

The woman with platinum blonde hair and green eyes put her little finger in her mouth.

'Hey!' she said. 'For an old guy, you're not bad-looking. She sipped some champagne from her glass. Then she smiled. She smiled, and suddenly her whole face changed. Before, she had looked like a naughty child. Now she was a beautiful woman. She had high cheek-bones below her beautiful green eyes. She had a long, straight nose and a wide mouth. Her shiny blonde hair was cut short. Her eyes were shining as she looked straight at me.

'Yeah!' she went on. 'You really don't look too bad. Do you know something, mister? I could fall for[2] a guy like you.'

What could I say? I'm in my early thirties – well, that's what I tell people. The truth is that I'm nearer forty, and the woman I was looking at couldn't have been a day more than twenty-three. I meet lots of women in my line of work[2], but I rarely[4] meet anyone as beautiful as this one. And on the few occasions when I have met a real stunner[4], she certainly hasn't wanted to have anything to do with me.

Still, the woman had a point[2]. I'm not bad-looking – dark hair, brown eyes, good teeth, nice clothes. And I've kept myself in shape[2]. I go to the gym three times a week. It's true that my face shows the marks of my time as an amateur[4] boxer. There are some small scars round my eyes, and my nose isn't quite straight any more – somebody broke it in a fight.

'The only problem,' the woman continued, 'is your job. No one ever got rich by doing your job. And I like expensive things.'

She smiled again. She had another point! I was sure that she spent a lot of money, and I certainly wasn't rich.

I'm a private investigator – that is, a private detective – in Los Angeles, California. My clients are often people who live on the edges of L.A. society[4]. Protection, security, blackmail, corruption, missing persons, small crimes[4] – these are the things I deal with every day. Sometimes, I even have a murder case. The only jobs I don't do are divorce cases and marriage problems.

My life isn't easy, but there is usually enough money each month to pay the rent for my apartment and the rent for my office. But there isn't any place in my life for a woman who looks like a million dollars[2] and dresses as if she *had* a million dollars. And the woman I was looking at now was obviously one of those!

'Still, what the hell[2],' the blonde said. She put down her glass of champagne and took a step towards me. 'Come on, Charlie, we're alone tonight. Kiss me.'

Charlie? My name's not Charlie. It's Lenny, Lenny Samuel. Some people call me Len. Still, I wasn't going to argue. I stood up and took a step towards the blonde.

'Hey, fella[3], sit down!' a man's voice shouted.

The blonde smiled. I opened my arms.

'Hey, fella! I told you to sit down!' the man shouted again.

I stared into the blonde's beautiful green eyes. Then I felt a hand on my shoulder.

'Sit down! *Now!*' the voice said.

I turned around. The man standing behind me was taller than me, and heavier. I'm one-metre-ninety tall, and I weigh just over ninety kilos – all muscle! But this guy was bigger than me in every way. And he was angry.

'Sit down, fella!' he shouted. 'I can't see the screen if you stand there!'

I sat down and I looked up at the movie screen again. Now the blonde actress was kissing a man. It was a close-up shot[1].

The woman was thirty metres away from me and her face was five metres high. Her name was Gail Lane. She was the hottest actress[1] in Hollywood, and this was the closest I had ever got to her!

'I'm sorry, fella,' I said to the man behind me. 'I guess I got carried away[2].'

I go to the movies a lot, especially when business is bad. And just then, business was very bad indeed. My last case had ended a few weeks before. Someone had stolen a racehorse from a beautiful woman. I'd found the horse, but I hadn't earnt any money. Since then, I'd tidied my office, cleaned my car, gone to the gym a lot, and waited for the phone to ring. It hadn't rung. I didn't have any new clients. So, most days, I went to the movies.

—

The movie ended and the lights came on. I got up and went to the men's washroom. There was a floor-to-ceiling mirror there, and I stood in front of it and looked at myself. It was true – I wasn't bad-looking. I was wearing a black leather jacket, a bright checked shirt and a pair of new black trousers. My brown Timberland boots completed the picture.

I took out my dark glasses and put them on. 'Cool[3]!' I said to the mirror, and I walked out of the movie theatre[1].

It was just before midnight. I decided that I didn't need the dark glasses. I walked round the corner to the parking lot[3], and I got into my old grey Chrysler. Then I drove slowly past the bars and clubs, trying to decide what to do. It was too early to go to bed. But it was too late to start calling friends to see if they wanted to go out. I was bored. I wanted something to happen.

I was just passing the Purple Palace, one of L.A.'s most expensive nightclubs, when something did happen. A shiny, white open-top car suddenly pulled out from the sidewalk[3]. I hit the brakes[2] and the Chrysler stopped. But the white car didn't stop. It hit the side of the Chrysler with a loud crash!

I was OK. I got out of the car. The Chrysler was OK too – they don't make cars like that any more. But the white car wasn't OK and neither was its driver! The front of the car was badly smashed, and oil was running out from under the engine. The driver was still sitting at the wheel and there was some blood on his face.

The driver of the white car was wearing a smart suit and he had short, well-cut hair. He looked about twenty-five, but his hair was steel grey.

After a few moments, he opened the car door. He walked towards me with an angry face.

'I'm going to make you pay for this,' he said.

He tried to grab my arm. His breath smelt of whisky. Then he tried to hit me. He tried, but he didn't succeed. I used to be a boxer, and this man was drunk! I leant back, and the blow missed. I was about to knock the man to the ground, when he suddenly closed his eyes and fell over. I hadn't touched him.

I felt a hand on my shoulder.

'That guy's a fool,' a voice said.

I turned around. It was a woman with platinum blonde hair and beautiful green eyes!

'That guy's a fool,' a voice said. I turned around.

2

'What Do You Want Me to Do?'

'That guy's a fool,' Gail Lane repeated. 'I'm sorry, mister.'
I opened my mouth to say something but no words came out. I was standing in the middle of a busy street in downtown[3] L.A., with the hottest actress in Hollywood!

'Say something,' Gail said.

'Hey! Well! Mmm – What do you want me to do?' I managed to say.

'Well, let's start by getting my car off the road,' Gail said.

'Your car?' I asked.

'Yeah,' she replied. 'It's my car. He shouldn't have been driving it. He's had far too much to drink. The parking attendant brought the car round to the front of the club, and Mike took the keys. I argued with him, but he wouldn't let me drive.'

'Mike?' I asked.

'Do you repeat everything someone says?' Gail asked sharply. 'Mike Devine is his name. Have you ever heard of him?'

I had. Mike Devine was the son of Joel Devine, who was a rich and successful movie producer[1]. Mike had never done a day's work in his life. But he was never short of money – his father made sure of that. As a result, Mike Devine had got into lots of trouble. There were always stories about him in the newspapers – stories about gambling debts, accidents, women, things like that. Now, Mike Devine lay in the street next to my Chrysler.

Gail and I pushed the damaged white car to the sidewalk. A crowd of people was standing there, staring at us. Then someone recognized Gail. Suddenly, people started to point at us and talk.

Gail looked at me. She smiled and her face changed, just like it had in the movie. She touched my arm.

'There *is* something else you can do for me,' she said in a quiet, warm voice. 'I can't stay here. People have seen me. I've got to get home. Will you help me, please?'

'Sure,' I said. 'Let's go.' I was delighted. I was excited! Perhaps Gail would invite me into her apartment. There would be soft lights and soft music. Anything might happen!

She smiled at me again. 'You're a nice guy,' she said.

We walked over to the Chrysler. Mike Devine's eyes were open now. There was blood on his smart suit. When he saw Gail, he stood up and held on to the side of my Chrysler.

'Get into this guy's car before the police come, Mike,' Gail said to the young man.

She pulled Mike Devine by his jacket, opened the back door of the Chrysler, and pushed him in.

'Oh,' I muttered. 'You'd like me to take him home too?'

'He lives at 9002, Hollywood Boulevard,' Gail said sweetly. 'Thank you for your help.'

'It's a pleasure,' I replied. 'Please get in.' I opened the front passenger door.

Gail looked puzzled for a moment, then she laughed.

'No, thanks,' she said. 'I'm taking a cab[2]. Thank you again for your help.'

Her lips touched my cheek briefly, and then she was gone. She ran to the sidewalk, where the doorman of the Purple Palace called a cab for her. I watched her go, then I got into the Chrysler. There was a strange noise coming from the back seat. I turned round. Mike Devine was being sick. I opened the window and drove away. A few minutes later, Mike Devine was unconscious.

—

9002, Hollywood Boulevard, was a tall new building with windows of black glass. I stopped outside it and switched off the

Chrysler's engine. A doorman came out of the building and walked up to the car. He was a short, heavy man with a small moustache.

'Hey, you can't park here, mister,' the doorman said.

I pointed at the unconscious figure lying on the back seat. 'Does he live here?' I asked.

The doorman looked at Mike. Then he opened the back door of the car, and stepped away as the smell reached him.

'Yeah, he lives here,' the doorman replied. 'Apartment 501.'

'Help me to take him up to his apartment,' I said.

Together, the doorman and I carried Mike Devine into the hallway and across to the elevator[3]. The doorman came up with us in the elevator, and waited while I found some keys in Mike Devine's trouser pocket. I unlocked the apartment door.

'OK,' the doorman said. 'Are you a friend of Mr Devine?'

'Well, no,' I replied. 'But I'm a friend of a friend. Why?'

'We're very careful about who comes in and out of this building. But if you're a friend of Mr Devine's friend, then I guess you can go in,' the doorman replied. 'But you'll have to give me your name.'

I gave him one of my business cards[4].

'Huh! A private eye[4]!' the doorman muttered.

'A private detective,' I replied. 'But can you keep an *eye* on[2] my car?'

'OK,' the doorman replied and got back into the elevator.

I opened the apartment door and pulled Mike Devine into a big living-room. I knew at once that something was wrong. All the lights were on. Clothes and books were lying all over the floor. Paintings hung sideways on the walls.

'Where's the bathroom?' I asked Mike.

He muttered something and pointed to a door. I took him into the bathroom and turned on the shower – full power, ice-cold! Then I pushed him into the shower with his clothes on. He made a noise when the ice-cold water hit his face, but five

I pushed him into the shower with his clothes on.

minutes later, Mike could stand up on his own, with his eyes open. I threw him a towel.

'Get dried. Then put some clean clothes on,' I said. 'I'll wait for you in the living-room.'

I closed the bathroom door and started to look around the apartment more carefully. The living-room was a real[3] mess. The windows were open and the curtains were moving in the gentle wind. There was a corridor on my left. I guessed there were bedrooms behind the doors in the corridor.

I opened the first door quietly. I saw a large bedroom. It was decorated in white – white walls, white carpet, a huge white bed.

I stepped into the room and walked towards the bed. I don't know what I was looking for. Then I heard a noise behind me. Before I could turn round, something hit me on the back of the head. I guess I must have fallen heavily to the floor. But I was unconscious by then.

3

Mike Devine

I could feel hands touching my body. The hands turned me onto my side. Someone started to empty the pockets of my leather jacket. They took out my wallet, my business cards, my gun.

I opened my eyes a little. A face was looking at me. It had short blonde hair and green eyes, and it was smiling at me. I smiled back, but the blonde woman's face didn't change. I closed my eyes and opened them again. She was still smiling at me. I moved my head a little. It hurt!

'Sit up!' a voice said. It wasn't Gail Lane's voice. It was a man who spoke.

I opened my eyes wide and saw that I had been looking at a photograph of Gail. The photograph was on a low white bed-side table. Mike Devine was sitting on the edge of the bed. He was wearing a white bathrobe with PALM BEACH RESORT written on it. He was holding my gun. And he was pointing it at my head.

'Now,' Mike Devine said in a quiet, hard voice. 'Who are you? And what are you doing on my bedroom floor?'

I touched the back of my head. It still hurt. I looked at my watch. Two o'clock. I must have been unconscious for over an hour. Mike Devine had obviously woken up after the cold shower I had given him.

'You can see who I am,' I replied. 'You've got my business cards. Look in my wallet and you'll find my detective's licence. Then please give me my things back.'

Mike Devine laughed. The gun was still pointing at my head.

'I'm not that stupid,' he said, and he threw the wallet over to me. 'You open the wallet and show me your licence.'

I picked up the wallet and showed him my detective's licence.

'OK,' Mike Devine went on. 'Now tell me what you're doing here. My apartment has been wrecked, and you're lying on my bedroom floor.'

I told Mike what had happened, and how I had helped him to get home. He looked at me and shook his head.

'No,' he said after a moment. 'I don't remember a thing. And I don't believe you.'

He walked over to a phone by the bed and picked it up.

'Get me security,' he said. There was a pause.

After a few moments he spoke again. 'Security? Hi, this is Mike Devine in 501. I've got an intruder[4] here. Can you come up? No, I'm not in danger. I've got his gun.'

Mike hung up[2] and sat down on the bed.

'You're making a mistake,' I said.

'We'll soon find out,' he replied.

Two minutes later, someone rang the bell of the apartment door and Mike Devine went to open it. A moment later, he came back into the bedroom with another man. It was the doorman with the moustache – the man who had helped me carry Devine in from the car.

'Where's the intruder?' the doorman asked.

Mike Devine pointed at me. The doorman gave a short, loud laugh.

'He's a private eye,' the doorman said. 'He brought you home, and he and I carried you up here.'

Mike Devine looked at me in surprise. He threw my gun back to me.

'I'm sorry, fella,' he said.

'I've got a couple of questions,' I said to the doorman. 'Did you let anyone in here earlier this evening? And did anyone leave after I got here?'

'He's a private eye. He brought you home and he and I carried you up here.'

'The answer to both questions is no,' the doorman replied. 'I don't let people into apartments when the owner's out. And no one left. If anyone had gone out through the hallway, I would have seen them.'

Mike Devine thanked the doorman, then turned to me.

'There's one thing, Mr Samuel. I don't seem to have any money on me. Could you lend me fifty bucks[3]?'

I smiled. Rich people! They're the ones who've never got any money. I opened my wallet and gave Mike fifty dollars. He walked over to the doorman and gave him the money.

'There's no need to say anything about this to anyone,' Mike said.

The doorman thanked him and left the apartment.

I sat on the bed and thought about what had happened. Who had hit me on the head? Had Mike himself done it? If *he* hadn't hit me, there must have been someone else in the apartment. Certainly, someone had wrecked the living-room. Perhaps that person had hit me on the head when I came into the bedroom. But why?

I asked myself the question, but my head hurt and I felt tired. I couldn't think of an answer.

'Look,' Mike said. 'I'm sorry. It's late. Can I offer you a bed for the night? I don't know who's been here. Whoever hit you on the head must have got out while I was in the bathroom. Perhaps they thought they were hitting *me*.'

'But the doorman said that no one had left the building,' I replied. 'So perhaps they're still here somewhere. Or perhaps they're hiding in another apartment. But they must have a key to your apartment. The first thing to do is to make sure they're not still here.'

Together, we searched every room in Mike Devine's apartment. We found no one.

Suddenly, I had an idea.

'I won't take your offer of a bed for the night,' I said. 'My car's outside. The police will take it away if I leave it in the street any longer.'

'Put the car in the garage,' Mike said. 'There's a garage underneath the apartment building, and the elevator goes straight down to it.'

My idea had been a good one. Mike had told me something that I had already guessed.

'So, someone *could* have left the apartment, then taken the elevator down to the garage and driven away without the doorman seeing them,' I said.

At that moment, the phone rang. Mike Devine answered it.

'Yes,' he said. 'Yes, I see.' Then he hung up. He looked terrible.

'Who was it?' I asked.

'Someone I owe some money to,' he replied. 'He said that *he* wrecked the apartment. He said it was a warning. He said he was sorry he had hit you. He thought you were me! And he said that next time, he wouldn't wreck my apartment – he would wreck me!'

So the person who had hit me on the head was trying to frighten Mike Devine. And he had succeeded. Mike was looking very frightened indeed.

'Mr Samuel,' Mike said. 'I think I need some protection. I will pay you to stay here for the rest of the night. Will two hundred bucks be all right?'

'Plus the fifty you borrowed,' I replied with a smile. I left the apartment, and went down to the hallway. I told the doorman I was staying for the rest of the night, then I went out into the street. Quickly, I drove the Chrysler into the underground garage.

—

Ten minutes later, I had turned off the lights in Mike Devine's living-room, and I was sitting in a comfortable chair with my gun beside me. Mike had gone to sleep in his huge white bed.

The hours passed. Nothing happened. There were no intruders. I didn't get any sleep.

The phone rang at six o'clock. I answered it.

'Mr Devine's apartment,' I said.

'Who's that?' a woman's voice asked. I knew that voice. It was Gail Lane.

At that point, Mike Devine picked up a phone in his bedroom and began to speak. I hung up immediately, so I never knew what she said to him.

4

Crazy Ellen's

I knocked on Mike Devine's bedroom door.

'It's Lenny Samuel,' I called through the door. 'I'm leaving now, Mr Devine. There's one of my business cards on the table in the living-room. You can send me the two hundred and fifty dollars later.'

Mike muttered something inside the bedroom. I didn't understand what he said. I left the apartment, got the Chrysler from the garage, and drove home. After a couple of hours' sleep, a hot shower and some clean clothes, I was a new man[2]. I drove downtown to my office building, parked the car, and went into Crazy Ellen's.

Crazy Ellen's is a bar, and a café, and a diner, and a meeting place. It's next to the building where my office is, on West Beaumont Drive. Don't ask me where the name of the bar came from. The owner of Crazy Ellen's isn't a mad woman called Ellen, or even a sane woman called Ellen. The owner is a man – an old Greek called Costas. I've known him for more years than I want to remember. I go to his bar a lot. People know that if I'm not in my office, I'll probably be at Crazy Ellen's.

'Hi, Len!' Costas shouted as I came in. It was shortly after nine o'clock and the place was empty. 'Hey, you look tired. Didn't you sleep?'

'Hi, Costas,' I said taking a seat at the bar. 'I'm OK. Give me some black coffee, some orange juice and a couple of fried eggs, please.'

I ate my breakfast and I chatted to Costas about baseball. Then I went to my office – two rooms on the fourth floor of an old building. On the floor of the waiting room, there was a pile

I ate my breakfast and I chatted to Costas about baseball.

of mail. I stepped over it and went through to my private room. There's not a lot to see – a desk, a couple of chairs, a grey filing cabinet, a window with a broken blind. I blew the dust off my chair and sat down at the desk.

The red light on the answerphone told me that some phone messages were waiting for me. I pressed the PLAY MESSAGES button. There were two messages.

The first message was from a man who didn't give his name. The message was short and simple. 'If you know what's good for you, Samuel, you'll take a holiday,' the voice said. 'Next time, it won't be just a little knock on the head.'

Interesting! This was a warning. And it was connected with Mike Devine in some way. But who was warning me? I didn't recognize the voice, and the caller hadn't left a number for me to phone.

But I knew the second caller as soon as he started to speak. It was a man called Rik. Rik Roma and I were old friends.

'Hi, Len, how are things?' Rik said. 'Listen, I may have a job for you. Can you meet me for lunch today? Give me a call.' And he left a phone number for me to call.

Rik's full name is Ricardo and he is Italian-American. His family came from Sicily in the 1930s. Rik and I worked together in the L.A.P.D. – the Los Angeles Police Department. My family is Hispanic – my full name is Leonardo, though people always call me Len or Lenny. My family came to the US from Puerto Rico. So Rik and I had something we could talk about.

Rik and I left the L.A.P.D. at about the same time. Rik went to work as a security man at a big movie studio[1] in Hollywood. I became a private eye. Rik had done very well over the years. He had been very successful in his work and he was now Head of Security at Magic Movie Productions. He always had new cars, and he lived in a luxury house in the hills, with two swimming pools. Me – well, I've got an old car, a small apartment, and a little wooden cabin[3] in the hills. You can guess how well I've done.

I called Rik and we arranged to meet at Gate Four of the Magic Movie Productions studios at one o'clock. I spent the rest of the morning at the gym in the basement of my office building. Then I had a quick shower and drove across town to the studios.

Rik was standing outside Gate Four. Rik is tall and thin, with a high forehead and short black hair. He has deep brown eyes. When he looks at you, you think he is looking *through* you.

I got out of my car, and Rik put his arm around my shoulder. Then he led me through the gate, showing his security pass[4] to the guard.

'You have to show a pass!' I laughed.

'Sure, Len, the security's real tight[3] here,' Rik replied.

We had lunch in the studio commissary – the movie studios' name for a restaurant – with fifteen nuns, twenty Japanese warriors, fifty English peasants, several princesses and a giant.

'We're making a fantasy movie in Studio Twelve,' Rik explained. 'These are the extras – they walk on and off the set[1] but they don't have speaking parts[1]. The stars and the other actors have their own private dining-rooms. They don't eat at the commissary.'

'So what other movies are being made here at the moment?' I asked. I have always been fascinated by movie-making since I was a child. I was really interested.

Rik laughed. 'We don't make very many movies here at the studios any more. Most of the studio area is used for tourism. We get lots of tourist groups visiting Hollywood. They come in to see the old sets – the sets of movies we made in the past. But now, most of our movies are made on location[1] – often in other countries. For example, many of the best people for special effects[1] are in England, so we often work there. And we shoot scenes[1] all over the world. Sometimes we do part of a movie here and then go on location for the rest of it.'

I was disappointed. I'd been hoping to see a movie being made. I told Rik this.

He smiled. 'I'll see what I can do[2],' he said. 'I'll try to arrange something after lunch. But before we eat, I want to ask you a question. Are you busy at the moment, or would you like to do a job for us? Something a little unusual?'

I didn't need time to think. 'Yeah,' I said. 'I'm pretty busy, but I guess I could do something for you.'

Rik laughed. 'You always were a bad liar! This is what it's about.'

He took a photograph out of his pocket and passed it over to me.

'Do you recognize her?'

Gail Lane was smiling at me from the photograph.

'Yes,' I replied. 'I spoke to her this morning!'

5

'Death Behind the Door'

I gave the photo back to Rik and I listened to him carefully. 'You obviously know who she is,' he began. 'But what do you mean about speaking to her this morning? She's working here at the studios today. She was on the set at seven o'clock.'

'Don't worry about it,' I replied. 'I meant that I dreamt about her. I was speaking to her in my dreams.'

'Yeah – so were a few million other men,' Rik said with a laugh. 'But this is serious, Len. Gail Lane is the hottest actress in Hollywood this year. The studio has invested[4] a lot of money in her. She's a big star in the US already, and she'll soon become a world star. That's why the things that have happened have worried the studio bosses[1] so much.'

'What *has* happened, Rik?' I interrupted. 'Tell me. You're being very mysterious.'

'Well, Len, I'll tell you.' Rik spoke quietly now, although the nuns at the next table certainly weren't listening to us. 'This is very secret. Only one other person knows about it. You must promise not to tell anyone about what I'm going to tell you.'

'If it's secret, why are you talking to me about it?' I asked. 'Why aren't you telling your own studio security staff?'

'Because no one else in Magic Movie Productions must find out about this,' Rik replied. 'Those are the orders of Homer Frank, the studio's chief executive[1].'

'Gail Lane is working on a movie here at the moment,' Rik went on. 'It's an international thriller, and the budget[1] is huge. We're spending hundreds of millions of dollars on this movie. So that makes Gail very valuable. And someone has been sending death threats.'

'Rik, do you mean that Gail Lane has been getting letters from someone who's threatening to kill her?' I asked.

'Not exactly[2],' Rik replied with a shake of the head. Then he paused while the waitress came to take our orders. I ordered tuna with a green salad and Rik ordered pasta.

'The threats were sent by e-mail[4], directly to Homer Frank,' Rik continued. 'Gail doesn't know about them. She hasn't been told. Mr Frank is afraid that she'll get scared.'

'I can understand that!' I said. 'I'd get scared if someone said they were going to kill me. What exactly did these messages say?'

'There were three messages, all sent during the last three days,' Rik answered in a low voice. 'They said, "*Death Behind the Door* will be the death of Gail Lane. Stop the movie or we'll stop her." All the messages were the same.'

I was puzzled. 'Sorry, Rik,' I said. 'I heard the words but I didn't understand them.'

Rik sighed. 'OK. I'll try again. Gail Lane is making a movie for Magic Movie Productions called *Death Behind the Door*. The message says that unless we stop making the movie, Gail will be killed.'

Our food arrived and we stopped talking for a few minutes. The tuna was great – it was juicy, with a lime and sweet pepper sauce. I was thinking hard while I ate it. Rik ate his pasta hungrily. There obviously wasn't anything wrong with that either.

'Rik, you've got to tell Gail about these threats!' I said, as we finished eating. 'She might not want to risk[4] being in this movie. You must give her the choice.'

'We can't afford to stop the movie, Len,' Rik said quietly. 'It's half-finished now. There are hundreds of millions of bucks invested in it. Mr Frank won't stop the movie. But we *are* going to protect Miss Lane. And that's where I want your help.'

'I don't think I'd be a good bodyguard[4], Rik,' I said quickly. 'Gail Lane is very attractive. I couldn't be near her and do the job properly.'

Rik laughed. 'No, no, Len,' he said. 'Gail already has two bodyguards, very good ones. I want you to join the movie crew[1], so that you're on the set all the time. I want you to keep an eye on everyone else. Perhaps these threats are just a hoax – a joke from a mad person. But we can't be sure.'

'OK,' I said. 'Five hundred dollars a day, plus expenses.'

'Four hundred,' Rik replied.

'Four-fifty,' I said.

'OK. Four-fifty,' Rik replied with a quick smile.

'But what will I do on the set?' I asked. 'I don't know anything about how movies are made.'

'You're going to be Miss Lane's adviser on detectives and investigations,' Rik said. 'In the movie, she plays[1] a private detective. You can tell her about how detectives work. You can start work tomorrow. And bring your passport with you.'

'My passport?' I asked. 'Why?'

'I said this movie is an international thriller,' Rik answered. 'We've finished the Asian scenes already. Today is the last day of shooting here at the studios. After today, the whole crew moves on to South America. When we've finished there, we'll go on to Europe.'

'What scenes are you shooting today, Rik?' I asked.

'Today's scenes will be shot with some of the stars' stunt-doubles[1],' Rik said. 'There's lots of fighting in today's scenes. There'll be blood everywhere – not real blood, of course!'

I ordered coffee. Rik wasn't telling me everything, I was sure of that. He was hiding something, but what? Perhaps I'd never know.

'But you said that Gail was working here today too,' I said. 'Can I watch the shooting for a while?'

Rik shook his head. 'Sorry Len. It's a closed set – that means no visitors. Carla Chapman, the director[1] of the movie, insists on that. She says that visitors always upset the actors.'

'But I'm not a visitor,' I said. 'I'm Miss Lane's adviser on being a detective. You said so yourself.'

Rik thought for a minute. 'OK, Len. There's not time to get you a security pass. But I'll get you onto the set using mine.'

We finished our coffee and left the commissary. A group of cowboys was just arriving. We walked over to Studio Nine. There was a big sign outside: DEATH BEHIND THE DOOR – SET CLOSED. Rik spoke to the security guards, who let us both in.

'Follow me,' Rik whispered. 'Be careful. It will be very dark inside. And don't make a noise, or Carla will kill us, and there really will be blood everywhere!'

We walked very quietly through the darkness of the studio. Everywhere, there were boxes and ropes, metal wires and electric cables. In the distance, we could see a bright light. When we got closer, we could see that it was a huge, bright blue screen, like a movie theatre screen. We could see someone hanging down on a rope in front of the screen.

'This is a blue-screen[1],' Rik whispered. 'Later, these shots will be combined with some shots of a rocky mountainside. When the audience sees the movie in a movie theatre, they'll think that the actor was really climbing a mountain!'

I watched in silence. I was fascinated. The person on the rope was still quite high up in front of the screen, at least fifteen metres from the floor.

Suddenly there was a loud scream, and the actor fell to the studio floor! Lights went on everywhere. We ran towards the person on the floor. It was a woman with short blonde hair.

'It's Gail!' I said to Rik.

We ran towards the person on the floor. It was a woman with short blonde hair.

6

The Bodyguards

There was a moment of silence on the set. Rik and I stared at the blonde woman on the floor. Then people came running from all directions. Rik took charge[2].

'Stand back!' Rik shouted. 'Get an ambulance!'

I was quickly pushed to the back of the crowd of actors and technicians[1] who came and stood around the woman. I walked slowly away from them. There was nothing I could do.

'Gail is dead,' I thought. 'She died in front of me, and I'm the man who was going to protect her.'

I felt terrible. I had wanted to protect Gail Lane. I had only met her once, but I had liked her very much, even if I didn't admire her choice of boyfriend.

Sadly, I walked towards some other sets which were not in use that day. After a minute, I came to one which was like the inside of a Japanese home. It looked like a real room, but there was no ceiling and there were only three walls. There were several doors which didn't open – there was nowhere to go. And I had nowhere to go now! Because of Gail's death, my job had finished before it had really started.

I left the Japanese room and walked slowly on, through half-built sets, and across open spaces. Studio Nine was the size of an aircraft hangar, and several Boeing 747s could have been parked inside it.

Ten minutes later, I saw something that I didn't believe! I saw her – Gail! Just for a moment, I saw her bright blonde hair, as a door near the end of the building opened and closed.

I couldn't believe it! Slowly and carefully, I walked towards the door. Soon I realized that I was looking at a row of dressing-rooms – the rooms where actors change their clothes and wait during shooting. Each dressing-room had a door and a window. There was a light on inside one of the rooms, though all the others were dark and empty.

I stepped quietly over to the lighted window and looked in. Gail Lane was sitting at a table with a cup in her hand. Her face was wet and her eyes were shiny. She had been crying.

I didn't have time to think about what I could see. As I looked through the window, someone grabbed my right arm and twisted it behind my back. I turned round and tried to grab my attacker. That was a mistake! My feet were kicked from under me. I fell to the floor and my attacker jumped on top of me. I struggled and I tried to get free. But my face was pressed against the floor, and the attacker was still holding my right arm. And now they had their knee on the back of my neck.

I tried to turn over. That didn't work. But my left arm was still free, so I reached behind my back and grabbed hold of a foot. I twisted the foot as hard as I could. There was a scream of pain from my attacker, and I quickly pushed them off my back. Then I dived, grabbing the person from behind. I forced the attacker to stand up with both arms held behind them.

The attacker suddenly started kicking my legs.

'Stand still or I'll really hurt you,' I said.

'Oh yes?' a voice said behind me. It was a woman's voice. Then two fists[4] hit me, low down on my back. The pain was terrible. Next, someone's fingers stabbed at the base of my neck, just above my shoulders. I let go of the person I was holding, and turned as quickly as I could. I turned just in time to receive a kick to the head. I spun around and fell heavily to the floor. Then I knew nothing!

When I woke up, I was still lying on the floor. A woman was sitting on my chest, holding me down. Another woman was sitting on my legs.

'Let me get up,' I said. 'I can explain why I'm here.'

'Josie's just been injured, and you're here looking into Gail's dressing-room window,' the woman on my chest said. She had shiny dark hair and was wearing a suit. 'And you haven't got a pass,' she went on. 'You'll stay where you are until someone from security comes.'

I lay on the floor for what seemed to be a long time. Then I heard footsteps.

'So you think you've caught him,' a voice said. I knew that voice. It was Rik.

The women got off me.

'There he is,' said the dark-haired woman. 'Take him away!'

I looked up at Rik.

'Sorry, Rik,' I said. 'I got lost. And then,' I pointed at the two women, 'these animals attacked me.'

'Fine,' Rik said. 'Let me introduce you to Annie and Arabella, Miss Lane's bodyguards.' He pointed at the women in turn. 'I told you they were good.'

Annie was the one with dark hair. Arabella had red hair and she was wearing a suit like Annie's.

'And who is he?' Arabella asked angrily.

'His name is Lenny Samuel. He's an adviser for Miss Lane,' Rik replied. 'He's going to advise her on how to behave like a private detective.'

'Oh, really!' Arabella laughed. 'What does he know? We caught him easily enough!'

'Wait!' I interrupted. 'What's happened? Gail Lane can't be in two places at the same time. If Gail is here in her dressing-room, who was that over there on the set?'

'The person who had the accident is called Josie. She's not dead, but she's quite badly injured. She was Gail's stunt-double – someone who did the most dangerous parts of Gail's acting,' Rik explained. 'The rope she was attached to broke. It was a terrible accident.'

'Let me introduce you to Annie and Arabella, Miss Lane's bodyguards.'

'Or a warning,' I said. I stood up slowly. My back and neck hurt. I shook hands with Annie and Arabella. 'I can see that Miss Lane is well protected,' I added.

'Yeah – when she wants to be,' Arabella replied angrily.

'What do you mean?' I asked.

'Sometimes she goes out at night without us,' Annie said. 'We can't protect her then!' She was angry too!

'Perhaps, after this accident, she'll be more careful,' I said.

'I'd like to introduce Mr Samuel to Miss Lane,' Rik said. 'But perhaps this isn't a good time.'

'Gail is very upset about Josie's accident,' Annie said. 'But I'll ask her if she'll meet Mr Samuel for a few minutes. I guess there won't be any more shooting today.'

Annie went into the dressing-room and closed the door behind her. We waited outside in silence. Then the door opened.

'Miss Lane will meet Mr Samuel for a few minutes. She can't talk for long – she doesn't feel well,' Annie said.

I followed Annie into the dressing-room. Gail was sitting at a table, holding a handkerchief. She looked up, and those green eyes were full of worry. She held out her hand.

'I'm pleased to meet you,' she said in a low voice. 'I'm sorry, I'm very upset. Josie was a friend as well as my double.'

'Mr Samuel will be advising you on how private detectives behave,' Rik explained.

Arabella laughed quietly.

Gail looked at me again more closely. I could feel her beautiful eyes staring at me.

'Haven't we met before?' she asked.

I thought for a moment. Arabella and Annie got angry when Gail went out without them – when she went out with Mike Devine, for example.

'No, Miss Lane,' I replied.

7

From L.A. to B.A.

Rik and I left Gail Lane's dressing-room and walked back to the set where the accident had happened. The police had arrived and were taking statements[4] from everyone. Rik and I told them what we had seen.

The area around the huge screen was closed off with yellow tape, and a number of detectives were carefully searching the floor there. A grey-haired lieutenant from the L.A.P.D. – a man called Dickinson – had taken charge. I had met him before. I asked him what he thought had happened.

'I don't know yet – it's hard to say,' Dickinson replied. 'The rope was checked before shooting started, and it was OK then. So why did it break?'

'Someone must have made a cut in the rope, to make it break easily,' I said.

'Mm —,' Dickinson said. 'You might be right. If you have any other ideas, call me. You know where to find me.'

Rik had to stay in the studio while the police detectives were making their investigation. I waited with him. I'm used to waiting and watching, and there was plenty to watch on the movie set.

Two hours later, the police had gone and Rik and I were sitting in his smart office.

'We'll have to shoot here for an extra day, because of Josie's accident,' Rik told me. 'Then the whole crew is moving to Argentina, to Buenos Aires. I want you to come along —'

Rik was interrupted by one of his phones ringing. He answered it.

'Yes, I see,' he said. 'I will, yes, sir. I will. I've got a new man here now.' He put the phone down. 'That was Mr Frank. He's had another e-mail. The message said, "This time we got the double. Next time it will be the star." Mr Frank is very worried.'

'So it wasn't an accident,' I said softly. 'And you told me it was a closed set, with no visitors allowed. So the person who cut the rope was probably someone working on the movie.'

Rik nodded. 'Yes. Or someone who had hidden in the studio before shooting started. We just don't know,' he said. 'That's why I want you to join us in Buenos Aires. I want you on the set all the time. Gail has Arabella and Annie with her whenever she isn't acting. But I want you to watch out for anything suspicious[4].'

'How many people are there in the movie crew?' I asked.

'There'll be two hundred and five of us flying to Buenos Aires,' Rik replied. 'And probably about two hundred Argentines will join us in B.A. You need a lot of people to make a movie.'

'And you want me to keep an eye on all of them!' I exclaimed.

Rik smiled. 'I'm sure you'll find out who has been threatening Gail,' he said. 'I know you, Len. You're always in trouble. Just stay with the crew and the trouble will find you.'

—

Two days later I was flying at ten thousand metres over Brazil, on my way to Buenos Aires. I sat back in the comfortable seat of the Aerolineas Argentinas Boeing 747, and I thought about what had happened during the past few days.

What was the relationship between Gail and Mike Devine? Why did someone want to stop the shooting of *Death Behind the Door?* Why was someone threatening to kill Gail? Who had injured Josie, Gail's double? And was he, or she, on the plane with us?

There were plenty of questions, but no answers! I looked at Rik, asleep in the next seat. There was certainly something he hadn't told me. I thought about Gail, sitting in the first-class section, at the front of the plane. I thought about the worry I had seen in her eyes at the studio.

Then I thought about Carla Chapman. She was also in the first-class section. I had met her briefly at the airport before we got onto the plane. Carla was one of Hollywood's best-known movie directors, a powerful and very hard-working person. She was a strong, proud, forty-five-year-old, with shoulder-length black hair and gold-framed glasses. At the airport, she had shaken my hand firmly, and she had said it was nice to meet me. Then she had told me to keep out of the way during shooting. After that, she had wrapped her long black coat around her and walked away.

I hadn't yet seen Brent Foster, Gail's co-star[1] in the movie. He was being flown to Argentina in his own private jet. I hadn't met him, but I felt that I knew him because I had seen so many of his movies. He always played bad guys, but he always got the girls! He looked a little like me, but he was younger and heavier, and he had blond hair and blue eyes. I was looking forward to meeting Brent.

After a while, I stopped thinking about my job and I looked out of the window at the clouds. I wanted to help Gail, but I had to wait for something new to happen.

It was mid-morning when the 747 landed at Ezeiza International Airport, outside Buenos Aires. There was mist in the air, and the weather was cool.

It took several hours to get all the baggage and equipment through customs. At last, it was done and we got into buses for the long journey to the city centre. Most of the movie crew were going to stay at the Bisonte Palace Hotel. In fact, we had booked all the rooms in the hotel. But Gail, Carla, Brent, and a few others were going to be at the luxurious Alvear Palace Hotel, near the Recoleta Cemetery[4], where we would be shooting.

There was no work till the next day, so after we had checked in at the hotel, I lay on my bed and fell asleep. When I woke, it was early evening and it was dark. I had a shower and then I went out for a walk. I was going to meet Rik and some of the members of the crew for dinner at ten o'clock – an early time for dinner in B.A.

I walked slowly through the streets, smelling the diesel smoke from the brightly painted *colectivo* buses. The streets were full of people. Young people were walking hand in hand, and large families were talking together on the sidewalks. Everyone seemed happy. I began to like B.A. very much.

I soon arrived at Corrientes, a long, wide street full of movie theatres, restaurants and cafés. I stopped at a place called Café Pernambuco and went in. Inside were groups of students talking excitedly, elderly men reading newspapers, and smartly dressed women eating cakes.

I ordered a coffee and sat back to enjoy the scene. After a while, I noticed a younger woman, sitting by a window. She was dressed in black, with a black scarf over her head. Her head was turned away from me, so I couldn't see her face. She looked at her watch again and again, and she looked up every time the café door opened.

I ordered another coffee and picked up a newspaper from a nearby table. From behind the newspaper, I could watch the woman in black without her seeing me. Suddenly, she turned her head towards me and called to the waiter.

I saw the woman's face. It was Gail Lane! I looked around the café. Where were Annie and Arabella, her bodyguards? Then I remembered Annie's words. 'Sometimes she goes out at night without us.'

Gail was alone. Who was she waiting for?

Suddenly, she turned her head towards me and called to the waiter.

8
Café Pernambuco

Gail spoke to the waiter. He smiled, and a few moments later, he returned with a cup of hot chocolate and a glass of water.

I watched Gail for half an hour, drinking my coffee slowly. Nobody joined her. I asked the waiter for some orange juice – too much coffee is bad for me. And I went on watching.

After another hour, and two more orange juices, I had to go to the men's washroom. When I came back, Gail was paying the waiter. She was about to leave. Had someone come in and spoken to her, or had she got tired of[2] waiting?

I made a quick decision. As Gail was standing up, I walked across the room as if I had just come in through the door. I walked up behind Gail and said in a quiet voice, 'Excuse me, Miss Lane, may I speak to you?'

Gail looked very frightened and she held on to the chair. Then she sat down.

I pulled out another chair. I sat down and looked at Gail. Her hands were white and they were shaking.

'So it was you,' she whispered. 'You!'

'What was me?' I asked.

'It was you who sent the message,' Gail whispered. 'Well, I'm here. What do you want?'

'Miss Lane, believe me, I didn't send you a message. I'm here by chance,' I said, looking into those beautiful green eyes.

'You're not who you say you are,' she said. 'You arrived at the studios on the day of Josie's accident. But I've seen you before. I know that.'

'You're right, Miss Lane,' I replied. 'We *have* met before. In the street outside the Purple Palace, in L.A. It was the night when Mike Devine crashed his car into mine. The night I took him home.'

Gail smiled for the first time. 'So that's who you are,' she said quickly. 'You helped me then and —'

She stopped speaking.

'And I'll help you now,' I said, finishing her sentence. 'I'm working for the studio and they've told me to do everything I can to help you. So here I am. What can I do?'

Gail smiled again. Then she looked sad. 'There's nothing you can do. There's nothing anyone can do.'

'Tell me your problem,' I said. 'What about the message you mentioned? What was the message?'

Gail opened her handbag, pulled out an envelope, and gave it to me. Inside it was a piece of Alvear Palace Hotel notepaper. I read the message.

If you want to have the photos, go to Café Pernambuco, Avenida Corrientes, at 7 p.m. Sit at a table by the window.

I put the note back into the envelope.

'What photos are those, Miss Lane?' I asked quietly. 'And what is so important about those photos? What makes you come to a café you don't know, to meet a person you don't know?'

Gail looked down at the table.

'I —' she started. 'I can't tell you,' she said. 'You wouldn't believe me, Mr Samuel.'

'Tell me,' I said, with what I hoped was a friendly smile.

Gail took a deep breath.

'You must keep this to yourself. Don't tell anyone,' she began. 'I'm being blackmailed[4]. Years ago, when I was much younger – when I was just starting to act – I was friends with a man. You need friends when you're a young actress. This man helped me to meet people who worked in the movies. It was all quite innocent – we were just friends. We'd go out for a meal or to see a show. Sometimes we'd go dancing in a club.'

'And the photos are of you and this man?' I interrupted.

'Yes, I believe so,' Gail replied. 'They're pictures of us dancing together at a club.'

I thought for a moment. 'And the name of this man? Is he someone important?' I asked.

Gail laughed. 'Important? No. Dangerous? Yes! I didn't know that when I met him. I thought he was a business man. I didn't know he was a gangster and a murderer. I thought he was just a kind person who was helping me to start working in the movies.'

'And his name?' I asked again.

'He's changed his name since I first knew him,' she replied. 'Vincenzo Calabrese was his name then. Vincent Calab is what he calls himself now. And now, he'll kill anyone who doesn't do what he tells them. He's a madman, Mr Samuel!'

This was very bad news! Vincent Calab was a well-known gangster. He was a ruthless[4] criminal and he had a gang of ruthless men to carry out his commands.

'So the message was from Vincent,' I said.

'No,' Gail replied. 'I've had similar messages before. This is from someone who's somehow got some photos of Vincent and me. The last message said that, unless I paid two hundred and fifty thousand dollars, the photos would be sent to the newspapers. Mr Samuel, if those photos are printed in the newspapers, my career will be finished.'

'If these messages aren't from Calab, have you any idea who *is* blackmailing you?' I asked. I wondered if it was someone working on the movie, but I didn't say so.

Gail shook her head. She picked up the envelope and opened her handbag. As she opened the bag, I saw a small gun inside it.

'I have to go,' Gail said. 'I don't think anyone is going to come.

'No. Perhaps they just watched you this time, to see if you

obeyed their instructions,' I said. 'I'll walk with you to the Alvear Palace. Downtown Buenos Aires is a safe place, but you're a star and someone might recognize you.'

'Don't worry about me,' Gail said. 'I've got something here to protect me.' She touched her handbag.

'If you're thinking of taking that gun onto the movie set tomorrow,' I said, 'forget about it. The security will be very tight here in B.A.'

'Then you take it,' Gail said with a smile. 'And give it to me tomorrow when we're on the set.'

'OK,' I replied. 'But let me walk back to the hotel with you now.'

Gail nodded. I paid the waiter for my coffee and orange juice, then we walked out into the evening air. It was quite a long walk back to Gail's hotel. We didn't talk a lot, but it was a peaceful, friendly time which both of us enjoyed. Outside the hotel, I said goodbye. I put Gail's gun into my pocket and I called for a cab to take me back to the Bisonte Palace.

As the cab drove through the busy streets, I was a happy man. Just before going into the hotel, Gail had kissed me on the cheek!

We walked out into the evening air.

9

Recoleta

'We start shooting tomorrow at nine, at the Recoleta Cemetery,' Rik said to me quietly, during dinner. 'I've hired a very good Argentine security company to search everyone who's working on location. I want you to stand with the security guys at the cemetery entrance, Len. You'll soon be able to recognize everyone.'

So the next morning at half past seven, I was standing at the entrance to the Recoleta Cemetery on Calle Junin, opposite Plaza Alvear. The Recoleta district is one of the richest and smartest in Buenos Aires, and the richest people in B.A. are buried in the graves in the cemetery. We were going to shoot a scene in the cemetery, a scene in which Gail – as a private detective – had a meeting with an international criminal – Brent.

That morning, Calle Junin was closed to traffic. Trucks full of movie equipment, buses for the extras, mobile dressing-rooms for the stars, and catering trucks[1] were all parked in the Calle Junin. Electric cables joined the lights and the other equipment to powerful generators[1] outside the cemetery.

Standing next to me was a man called José Luis, from the Argentine security company. His men and women were searching everyone as they arrived. In my jacket pocket was Gail's gun, in a mailing envelope. Fortunately, no one had decided to search me.

Gail and Brent Foster came from their mobile dressing-rooms, and stood at the cemetery entrance. Gail was looking worried. As soon as she had been searched, I gave her the mailing envelope.

'Excuse me, Miss Lane,' I said. 'This package is for you.'

Gail took the package and smiled at me for a moment. Then she walked into the cemetery.

By nine o'clock, Carla was ready to begin shooting. Huge lights lit up the front of one of the biggest tombs[4] in the cemetery. The tomb was built of white stone and it was the size of a small house. The front of the roof was decorated with life-size[4] white statues.

Two cameras were going to shoot the scene. One camera was lifted up in the air on a crane[1]. Another was on metal rails, laid on the ground. When she edited the scene back at the studios, Carla would edit together shots from the two cameras.

Carla sat in a big folding chair with DIRECTOR written on the back. When everybody was ready she shouted, 'Cameras! Action[1]!'

Brent Foster, wearing a white raincoat, walked along a path towards the camera on rails. Then he stopped by the front of the tomb. After a moment, Gail came running up to Brent.

'Cut[1]!' Carla shouted. 'Brent, I want you to look a bit more nervous. Gail, that was great – but I'd like you to look a little more excited, please.'

They repeated the scene seven times before Carla was satisfied. Then we all stopped for coffee. The make-up artists[1] repaired Brent and Gail's make-up. The cameras moved to new positions. Soon, another scene was being shot in front of the tomb. This time, it was a conversation between Brent and Gail.

I wasn't really bored, but there wasn't anything for me to do. Annie and Arabella were there to look after Gail, so I decided to take a walk around the cemetery. The tombs were magnificent. There were many styles of architecture, but all the tombs showed the wealth of the people buried in them.

I must have been walking around for half an hour before I decided it was time to go back and check on the shooting. I went towards the tomb where the movie crew was working. I was thinking about Gail, and the messages she had received, when I saw someone dressed in black lying on the ground beside the back wall of the tomb. I ran quickly to see who it was. It was Annie! Her hands were tied behind her back, and there was tape across her eyes and mouth.

I looked around carefully. I felt that someone was watching me, but I couldn't see anyone. I walked very quietly along the side of the tomb, towards the front. At that moment, something made me look up at the roof. Was someone hiding there? All I could see was the line of white stone statues – statues holding flowers, statues holding plants, statues holding books, statues holding huge stone balls. Then one of the statues with a stone ball moved. Was I dreaming? No! The statue took a step forward towards the front edge of the roof and then stood still again.

I ran around to the front of the tomb as fast as I could. Gail and Brent were still standing there, in the bright lights of the set. I looked up and saw the statue right above them. The heavy stone ball was now raised above its head. I dived forward, pushing Brent out of the way and throwing Gail to the ground.

'Cut!' shouted Carla.

Crash!

The heavy stone ball hit the ground just where the two stars had been standing. At that moment, Arabella jumped on top of me.

'Stay away from Miss Lane!' she shouted as she pulled me away from Gail.

'What do you think you're doing?' Carla shouted at me.

'There's no time to explain,' I replied, running around to the back of the tomb, closely followed by Arabella.

But we were too late. The statue had gone. Arabella untied Annie and took the tape off her face.

'What happened?' Arabella asked.

'Someone jumped on me from behind,' Annie muttered

I dived forward.

angrily. 'I don't know who it was.'

'Was it him?' Arabella asked, pointing at me.

'I don't know,' Annie replied. 'It could have been.'

We walked back to the set. I explained to Carla what had happened. Gail and Brent were OK. Gail was laughing nervously and Brent looked a bit shocked.

Then I found Rik and told him what had happened.

'I knew trouble would find you, Len,' Rik said with a smile. 'I was right!'

'No,' I replied. 'I was just lucky. I'm pleased that I was able to save Gail. But it was only luck. Why don't you call the police?'

Rik looked away from me. 'No, Len,' he said quickly. 'We don't want to involve the police. We have to go on to Istanbul in three days' time. We can't change the schedule[1]. We can't wait for an investigation.'

'OK, but there's another thing,' I said. 'I'm meant to be advising Gail on how private detectives behave. I haven't had a chance to speak to her about that yet.'

'Making you her adviser was just a way to get you onto the set,' Rik answered. 'Still, I suppose you're right. Gail and Brent are going to a tango show tonight with Carla and me. Why don't you come along with us? You can talk to Gail there.'

'OK,' I said. 'And one more thing. I need some transport of my own. This is a big city and I need to be mobile if I'm going to protect Gail.'

Rik thought for a moment. 'We can hire a car for you,' he said.

'A motorbike would be better,' I replied. 'It will be much quicker in heavy traffic.'

'I'll see what I can do,' Rik said.

I spent the afternoon on the movie set. I watched Brent and Gail acting the same scene again and again. Movie schedules are made up of short periods of hard work, followed by hours of standing and waiting. But no one tried to kill Gail. No one tried to sell her any photographs. Gail didn't need the gun. Arabella and Annie didn't attack me. No statues moved. I was bored.

When shooting ended for the day, Gail came over to me.

'I've got to talk to you,' she said, looking around to see if anyone was listening.

'Not here,' I said. 'There are too many people here. How about tonight at the tango show?'

She stared at me. 'How did you know about that? Our visit to the tango show was meant to be a secret.'

I laughed. 'I'm a detective!' I said.

10

Tango!

Just before ten o'clock that night, I was sitting on a shiny Harley-Davidson motorbike, parked by the sidewalk opposite the Alvear Palace Hotel. Rik had hired this stunning machine for me to use while we were in B.A. To match the Harley-Davidson, I was wearing a black suit with a blue tie and a white silk scarf, and a blue crash helmet.

I watched the doors of the hotel carefully. At ten o'clock, Carla and Brent came out. A few moments later, they were followed by Gail who was wearing a long green dress. The three of them stood together on the sidewalk.

Suddenly, a black limousine stopped beside them, and I saw Rik in the front of the car, next to the driver. Carla, Brent and Gail got into the back of the limo, which drove off down Avenida Alvear. I waited until it was a hundred metres ahead of me, then I moved the Harley-Davidson out into the traffic behind it.

After a short time, the limo turned on to the wide street called Avenida 9 de Julio[4], driving towards the La Boca district. I followed, but I stayed a hundred metres behind it. From that position, I soon noticed a red Ford, which was driving about sixty metres behind the limo.

'It's just a coincidence,' I thought. But when we left the Avenida 9 de Julio and started to travel through much smaller streets, the red Ford stayed in the same position. By the time we reached the narrow alleys of the La Boca district, it was obvious that the Ford was either following the limo, or that the people in it were going to the same tango show.

The limo stopped in a dark street, outside what looked like a large private house. The four passengers got out of the car and went into the house. The limo drove away. I slowed down and watched the red Ford. It parked fifty metres away from the large house and two young men got out. They were wearing smart suits, and they had short hair. They walked quickly along the street and went into the house. I locked the motorbike and walked up to the red Ford. There was a copy of the *Buenos Aires Herald* on the back seat. 'That's interesting,' I thought. 'An English language newspaper. Perhaps the men are just tourists.'

I went into the house. A waiter led me into a restaurant with long tables and a stage at one end. I joined Rik, Carla and the movie stars at one of the tables.

For a couple of hours, we ate. It was an excellent meal, and then – at midnight – the dancing started. The show was great! It was loud, exciting, and very lively. But there was something sad about the music. After an hour, I had discovered that at an Argentine tango show you only watch the performance – you don't have to dance yourself. I was pleased about that!

But I was sitting next to Gail who wasn't pleased about it. 'I want to dance too,' she said.

'You can't,' I replied. 'These are professional dancers who have spent their lives dancing the tango. They don't want an American amateur[4] joining in.'

'I'll show you,' Gail said, standing up quickly.

A dance was just finishing, and before I could stop her, Gail had jumped up onto the stage. I called one of the male dancers over to our table, and I spoke to him briefly in Spanish. He nodded and smiled. Then he went back to the stage, and when the music began again, he started to dance with Gail.

She was fantastic! Gail danced the tango as if she had been born in Buenos Aires. We watched her in great surprise. So did the two young men in suits, who were sitting at another table!

At the end of the dance, the other dancers applauded Gail while she walked back to our table. When she sat down, her face was bright with excitement.

'I'm an American amateur, am I, mister?' she said. 'And what did you say to that dancer?'

I thought for a moment. Then I told a lie. I wanted Gail to be happy. 'I said that you were a famous American dancer,' I replied. 'I said that he would enjoy dancing with you.' In fact, I'd told him that Gail couldn't dance the tango, but that it was her birthday and she wanted to celebrate.

Soon, Brent, Carla and Rik went to the bar. Gail and I were alone.

'You said you wanted to talk to me, Gail,' I said quietly.

'I suppose I should thank you for saving my life at the cemetery,' Gail said. 'Everything happened so quickly this morning. If you hadn't been there, that stone ball would have killed me.'

I nodded. 'Perhaps. You were very brave,' I said. 'Have you had any more messages?'

Gail shook her head. 'No,' she said. 'Do you think that the person who has the photos is trying to kill me?'

'I don't know,' I replied. 'But I don't think so. Whoever has the photos – he wants you alive, so that you can pay for them. But whoever dropped the stone – he wanted you dead!'

Gail opened her handbag. 'Here's the gun,' she said, giving me the package. 'Will you bring it onto the set for me again tomorrow? I feel much safer with it.'

'OK,' I said and I quickly put the envelope in my pocket as I saw Brent, Carla and Rik returning to our table.

'Are you having fun?' Rik asked.

'Sure,' I answered. 'We're just talking about being a private eye.'

'I don't believe you're a detective at all,' Gail said with a sudden smile. 'Prove it!'

'Right,' I said. 'Do you see that table in the corner, by the door?'

'The table with two men in dark suits sitting at it?' Gail replied.

'Yes, that's it,' I said. 'Those two men followed you here. I'm going outside now. When I've gone, you go over to their table and ask them why they were following you. I think that that will make them leave. And then I'll follow *them*. I'll find out who they are.'

'OK,' Gail said, 'let's try it!'

I left the tango show and I went and sat on the Harley-Davidson. I put the gun into one of the motorbike's big carriers. My guess was right! Two minutes later, the men in suits came hurrying out of the house and got into the red Ford. The engine started at once, and they drove off as fast as they could along the narrow streets. I followed them carefully.

Soon we were out on the straight, wide Avenida 9 de Julio again, and I had to stay closer to the Ford so that I didn't lose it in the traffic. The Ford increased its speed and so did I.

'They've seen me,' I thought.

Soon we were both travelling at over a hundred and twenty kilometres per hour. It was nearly two o'clock, but there was still a lot of traffic on the streets.

The red Ford moved easily between the slower cars – the driver was very clever. He was very clever, but it was easy for me to follow the Ford on the big motorbike.

I got behind the Ford for a moment, but it accelerated again. It went through a red traffic light, and I followed it. So did a police car! A few moments later, I heard the sound of the police car's siren[4] behind me. Then I saw the flashing light as the police car came alongside me. A policeman in the front of the car shouted at me to stop. So I slowed down and stopped. The red Ford drove on at high speed down the wide avenue.

'*Que pasa?*' a tall policeman asked me, as we stood by the side of the road.

He told me to get off the motorbike and get into the back

Two minutes later, the men in suits came hurrying out of the house and got into the red Ford.

of the police car. There was another policeman in the car. He asked me, in Spanish, for some identification. I gave him my passport. He looked at it for a minute. When he spoke again, he spoke in English.

'So,' the policeman said, as he handed my passport back to me, 'you are a visitor to this country. But you think you can break all the traffic laws – speeding, dangerous driving, going through red traffic lights —'

'I can explain, officer,' I began.

'My name is Garcia, Captain Roberto Garcia,' the policeman said.

'Captain Garcia,' I began again. 'I can explain.'

I told the policeman about my job, about the movie, about Gail and about the two men in the red Ford.

'Yes, we saw the men in the red Ford,' the captain said.

'And why did you stop me, and not them?' I asked.

Captain Garcia smiled and shook his head. 'I couldn't stop the car you were following. It had diplomatic licence plates[4],' he said.

'Diplomatic plates? Which embassy did the car belong to?' I asked, although I was sure I already knew the answer.

'The United States of America, *señor*,' Captain Garcia replied.

11

Misunderstandings and Messages

I sat in the back of the police car on the Avenida 9 de Julio and waited for Captain Garcia to charge[4] me. I waited for him to charge me with speeding, dangerous driving, and going through red traffic lights. But he didn't charge me. Instead, he took out a notebook and wrote something in it. Then he tore out the page he had written on.

'I believe your story,' the captain said, 'but you must obey our traffic laws. I'm not going to charge you this time. But if we catch you riding your motorbike dangerously again, you'll be in serious trouble.'

I nodded.

'And one more thing,' the captain said with a smile. 'Here's my phone number.' He passed me the piece of paper from his notebook. 'If I can help you in any way, call me.'

'*Muchas gracias*,' I said.

I got out of the police car and onto the motorbike. As I rode away – very slowly – on the Harley-Davidson, I thought that I had been very lucky. What would the captain have done if he had searched the motorbike and had found Gail's gun?

—

At seven-thirty the next morning, I was back at the Recoleta Cemetery. I was standing by the gate with the Argentine security chief, watching everyone being searched. I had already seen Rik and told him about the chase the night before and about my meeting with the Buenos Aires police. I didn't tell him about the gun.

A line of technicians and actors was waiting to be searched. It was quite cold and the people in the line were becoming impatient. Because of the problem of the day before all the security guards were very careful and the search was taking a long time. I saw Annie and Arabella near the front of the line and I waved to them. I was trying to be friendly.

'Why aren't you being searched?' Arabella shouted to me.

I smiled and shook my head. But when it was Arabella's turn to be searched, she refused. There was an argument with one of the Argentine security guards. Minutes went by and the other people in the line were becoming more and more impatient. The security guard called for help on his radio, and Rik came running across to the gate.

'Hey, what's all this?' Rik asked Arabella. 'You know the rules – everyone's got to be searched.'

'I know that,' Arabella replied. 'I don't mind being searched – but only after they've searched this guy.' She pointed at me. 'He hasn't been searched – he's just standing and watching.'

Now everyone was looking at me. I called to Rik and he came to speak to me. 'There's something I've got to tell you, Rik,' I said, very quietly.

'Not now, Len,' Rik replied. 'Get over to the front of the line and let them search you. We must start shooting on time today.'

'Rik, there's been a misunderstanding —' I said.

'Come on!' Arabella shouted. 'What's the matter? Have you got something to hide?'

I didn't move.

'If he won't let the guards search him, we'll search him ourselves,' Annie said. And before I could do anything, she and Arabella ran over and started to search my clothes. They didn't find anything in my jacket or trousers.

Then Arabella said, 'Take off your boots.'

Very, very slowly, I took off my boots. Annie picked them up, turned them upside down, and shook them. The package with Gail's gun in it fell out of my left boot. Annie grabbed the envelope, tore it open and held the gun in the air.

The package with Gail's gun in it fell out of my left boot.

'I knew that there was something wrong about that guy,' Arabella said.

Rik took the gun. He was very angry.

'Samuel,' he shouted, 'you're fired[4]! Go back to your hotel and wait for me there!'

He turned to Annie and Arabella. 'Well done! Now let's get on with the search so we can start shooting.'

I turned and walked away. I got onto the Harley-Davidson and drove it slowly back to the hotel. I waited for Rik in reception. I felt terrible. I had been a fool. Why had I agreed to take Gail's gun onto the set for her? It was a stupid thing to do!

An hour later, Rik came into the reception area of the Bisonte Palace.

'Why did you do it, Len?' he said, shaking his head. 'Why were you carrying a gun? You knew we would search everyone today.'

'It's Gail's gun,' I explained. 'I was bringing it onto the set for her. She's frightened.'

'Well, you were stupid!' Rik said. 'You can't stay here any longer. You'll have to go back to L.A. Wait there for instructions from me. We've only got three more days here, before we move on to Turkey. I'll try to find a way for you to join us in Istanbul. It's very important that nothing bad happens to Gail.'

Rik thought for a minute. 'Hey! I've got an idea. I know how we can get you onto the set in Istanbul. You can be one of the extras!'

'But people will recognize me,' I said.

'No they won't,' Rik said. 'Not after the make-up artists have finished working on you!'

Rik made some phone calls and booked me a flight to L.A. on American Airlines. The flight was leaving that afternoon. I packed my case, wrote a note for Gail which I left at the Alvear Palace, and returned the Harley-Davidson to Rik. Then I took a cab to Ezeiza Airport.

I checked in and went to sit on the high balcony overlooking the airline desks. I bought a coffee and I thought again about what had been happening. Who had sent Gail the messages about the photographs of her with a gangster? Who had injured Josie and tried to kill Gail? And how was the US Embassy involved? I didn't have answers to any of these questions.

Before I went to the plane, I made three phone calls. One was to Captain Garcia. I explained that I had to leave Argentina, but I didn't explain why. I told him I was worried about Gail. He replied that there wasn't much he could do when she was on the set. But he said he would arrange for her to be guarded for the rest of the time.

My second phone call was to L.A. I called an old friend called Toni Trenton. She was a journalist on the *L.A. Messenger*. She wrote about crime and criminals. Years ago, I had been in love with Toni, but that wasn't why I called her. I asked Toni to find out all she could about three people – Gail Lane, Mike Devine and Vincent Calab.

My third call was to myself. I called my answerphone in L.A. to find out if there were any messages for me. There was only one. I listened to it. It was brief. 'Samuel,' the voice said. 'You've got to help me. I'm in desperate[4] trouble. Please call me on 818–558–5898.'

I recognized the voice. It was Mike Devine.

12

Lunch and Information

When I got back to L.A., it was late evening. I was very tired. I went straight to my apartment and I went to bed.

The next morning, I was up early and went for a run in the park. I was still tired, but I felt better after a shower and a good breakfast. I got into the Chrysler and drove downtown to my office.

I stopped at Crazy Ellen's for a coffee and a chat with Costas.

'Have you been away, Len?' Costas asked.

I told him where I'd been.

'Some people have been looking for you,' Costas said. 'They said they knew you often came in here.'

I drank my coffee slowly. 'It's nice to be popular!' I thought.

'Can you remember what these people looked like?' I asked.

Costas has a very good memory – he is proud of it.

'Well,' he said, wiping the bar with a cloth, 'the first visit was yesterday morning. Two heavies[4] came in here. They were real big guys, in their twenties, with mean faces. Real tough guys. They weren't police. I think they were carrying guns. They said they wanted to see you about a bet.'

'That's strange,' I thought. But I'd been involved in a case about a missing racehorse a few weeks before. Some bad guys had been making illegal bets. Perhaps the heavies' visit was connected with that.

'And the second visit?' I asked Costas.

'Also yesterday, in the afternoon,' he said. 'A young guy, about twenty-five, although he had grey hair. He looked rich. But he seemed really worried.'

'Mike Devine,' I thought. I finished my coffee.

'Many thanks, Costas.' I said.

I left Crazy Ellen's and went to my office. There had obviously been some visitors there while I had been away. They had emptied all the drawers of my desk and my filing cabinet onto the floor. That was OK. I never keep anything important at the office because people come and search it while I'm away! I picked up some of the papers and put them back in the filing cabinet. Then I sat down at my desk and I called Mike Devine. His answerphone took the call, and I left a message – Mike was probably still asleep.

After that I called Toni Trenton and arranged to meet her for lunch. She said she'd already got some information for me. We arranged to meet at Pastroudi's Italian restaurant at one o' clock. I spent the rest of the morning tidying my office and calling Mike Devine. But Mike didn't pick up his phone – his answerphone took the calls again.

I walked to Pastroudi's – it wasn't far from the office. I was sitting at my favourite table by the window when Toni came in. She had blue eyes, short dark hair and a warm smile. She was wearing a smart blue trouser suit. She looked great. I almost fell in love again!

Then I remembered why we had broken up[2]. It had been nearly fifteen years before. Toni had said I had to choose between her and boxing. She didn't like to see me being knocked about[2]. I had chosen boxing and she now had a successful career as a crime reporter on the *L.A. Messenger*.

Toni kissed me on the cheek and we spent five minutes talking about what we had both been doing. I told her about Gail and Argentina. She told me about crime in L.A. Then we ordered our food.

'Right, Lenny,' Toni said when the waiter had gone. 'You asked me about three people. Do you want to hear about them?'

I smiled and nodded.

She looked great. I almost fell in love again!

'OK. First, Mike Devine,' Toni said. 'He was the easiest – there's so much written about him in the papers. He's a playboy[4]. He goes out partying[4] most nights. He's only interested in pleasure.'

'And he has lots of money,' I added.

Toni looked at me. 'Not any longer,' she said. 'At least, that's what people are saying. His father got tired of paying Mike's debts, and told him to stop partying and get a job. Mike didn't listen, so old Joel Devine stopped giving him money.'

'So where does Mike Devine get his money now?' I asked.

'He's been borrowing lots of money – from banks, from people he knows, from everywhere. That's what people are saying. Now he's head over heels in debt[2],' Toni replied. 'Now, do you want to hear about Gail Lane next?'

'Yes, please,' I said as the waiter brought our food. Toni had seafood and rice, and I had lobster.

Toni ate her lunch and told me Gail's story.

'Gail's interesting,' she said. 'You know about her friendship with Mike Devine, of course. I think that he's been borrowing money from her too. That's one thing. You'd think that it would be easy for me to find out lots of other things about a movie star. But it wasn't easy! Nobody knows much about her. Gail became a star quite recently. Before that, she certainly spent time with gangsters. I'll tell you more about that in a minute. But some people say that recently she's also been involved with[2] a US Senator[4] – Senator Theo Z. Democrates.'

I knew about Senator Democrates. He was from a Greek family. He was single – he had never married. And he was one of the most powerful men in the government. He was the chairman of an important government committee. He was also a multi-millionaire.

'Mmm, that's interesting,' I said. 'Democrates is an honest man, but he has a reputation for ruthlessness[4]. And a lot of ruthless people work for him.'

I ate my lobster thoughtfully. Some things were beginning to become clear.

'Vincent Calab was the third name,' Toni said, 'and I expect you know a lot about him already. He's a ruthless man too! He's a gangster from Chicago who moved here ten years ago and got involved with the movie industry[2]. People say that he has been laundering[4] money. They say he invests illegal money – stolen money – in movies. When the movies make a profit, he gets his money back, and then the money is legal. Lots of criminals do that kind of thing. Hollywood could be a good place to do money-laundering. Making movies takes a lot of money.'

'Yeah, I see what you mean,' I said.

'Calab's an unpleasant man,' Toni went on. 'He's a madman. He's very violent. He kills anyone who works against him. But the police have never been able to charge him with any crime. He's really very dangerous, because he isn't quite sane. Some people call him Mad Vince. I hope you're not getting involved with him, Lenny.'

'No,' I replied. 'But I think Gail Lane was innocently involved with him some years ago.'

'Yes,' Toni said. 'I heard about that too. Stay away from Calab, Lenny. He's a very bad guy.'

I didn't reply. I was thinking about the 'visitors' who had searched my office. I thought they were the two heavies that Costas had told me about. And I also thought they might be Calab's men. Perhaps I was involved with him, whether I liked it or not.

We finished eating. I thanked Toni for her help and asked if I could borrow her mobile phone. I dialled Mike Devine's number and this time I got a reply.

'Come to the apartment, will you?' Mike said. 'I need your help.'

Toni and I sat and talked for a little while longer. Then, as usual, we argued over who was going to pay for the meal. As usual, Toni won the argument. She was still sitting at the table when I left Pastroudi's. She was lovely. Perhaps I had made a mistake when I chose boxing, I thought. A big mistake!

13

Miss Sullivan and Mr X

I took a cab to 9002, Hollywood Boulevard. The doorman with the moustache recognized me, and he called Mike Devine to tell him I was on my way up to Apartment 501. Mike was waiting by the elevator and led me into his living-room. He looked tired and worried.

'What can I do for you, Mike?' I asked as I sat on a white sofa.

'Why didn't you call me back before?' Mike Devine asked angrily.

I smiled. 'Firstly, because I was in Argentina. And secondly, because I'm still waiting for you to pay me two hundred and fifty dollars,' I replied.

'Oh, I'm sorry. I guess I forget about that,' Mike said and took out a chequebook. He quickly wrote a cheque and gave it to me.

'Is this a good cheque?' I asked, waving it in the air. 'Will your bank pay me the money?'

'Of course it's a good cheque!' Mike said angrily. 'What do you mean, Samuel? What do you know?'

'You told me you were in big trouble. And I heard a story that it was money trouble,' I said. 'So I wondered if there was any money in your bank to pay this cheque.'

Mike Devine put his hands over his face. 'You're right,' he said in a dull voice. 'I'm broke[3] – I haven't got a cent. But that's not all. I'm in worse trouble than that.'

'Do you want to tell me about it?' I asked and I sat back on the sofa.

Mike began to speak. It was a long story, and Toni Trenton had told me some of it already. Mike had borrowed money from everyone he knew. Then, a week before, he had had a visitor.

'It was the day after you brought me home from the Purple Palace,' Mike explained. 'In the afternoon, the doorman called to say there was a woman to see me. A woman called Miss Mary Sullivan. I didn't recognize the name, but I have a lot of friends —' He waved his hand in the air. 'Anyway, the woman came up here and I asked her what she wanted.'

'What did she look like?' I asked.

'Mid-thirties, nice clothes, short brown hair. She talked in a very polite and formal way,' Mike replied. 'But what she said really frightened me.

'She said that she represented[4] a powerful person,' he went on. 'She called this person Mr X – she wouldn't give me his real name. She said that Mr X had bought most of my debts. He had paid the people I had borrowed money from, so now I owed the money to him. Over eight hundred thousand dollars, she said.'

'Wow!' I said, 'that's a lot of money.'

'And Mr X wanted his money now, the woman told me,' Mike continued. 'I explained that I couldn't pay. Even this apartment is owned by my father. Then Miss Sullivan said that there was another way for me to pay off the debt. I had to leave L.A. at once and promise never to see Gail Lane again. If I kept my promise for a year, Mr X would forget about the debt.'

'And what did you say?' I asked.

'What could I say?' Mike Devine replied. 'I agreed to go. Miss Sullivan gave me seventy-two hours to leave L.A.'

'But you're still here, Mike,' I said.

Mike Devine started to cry. 'Yes, I can't go. I can't live without Gail. I love her, even if she doesn't love me. And all my friends are here in L.A. I don't know where to go.'

'Have you heard from Miss Sullivan again?' I asked.

'Yes, the day before yesterday,' Mike replied. 'That's why I called you. She told me that I had broken our agreement by not leaving. I asked for more time and she gave me until tomorrow morning. She said that I had to call her tomorrow evening, from somewhere a long way from L.A.'

'Did she say what would happen if you didn't leave L.A?' I asked.

'Yes, she said that I had cheated people and told lies to get money from them. She said I would go to prison.' Mike Devine stopped. Then after a while he spoke again, slowly and sadly. 'All my life I've had everything I've wanted,' he said. 'If I went to prison, I would have nothing. My father won't help me. He says that prison would be good for me. But he's wrong! I would die if I went to prison. You've got to help me, Samuel. What can I do?'

I smiled. 'Well I don't have eight hundred thousand dollars to lend you,' I said. 'My advice is to do what Mr X wants.'

'But I'm broke. I don't have any money at all. I can't afford[2] to stay anywhere,' Mike replied.

'Well, I've got a cabin up in the hills, at a place called Crystal Lake,' I said. 'It's a long way from L.A. I suggest you go there now and do what Miss Sullivan told you to do. Call her tomorrow evening and give her the number of the cabin. She will call you back. Then she'll know that you've really left L.A. And I'll try to find out who Mary Sullivan is, and who her boss, Mr X, is. Give me her phone number.'

Mike gave me the number, and I told him how to find Crystal Lake. I gave him the name of a farmer there who kept a key to my cabin. I hadn't been up to Crystal Lake for many months. It was a place I used to go to when I wanted to do some fishing. Over the years, I had caught a lot of fish in the lake near the cabin.

'I don't know how to thank you,' Mike Devine said. 'You must think I'm a bad person.'

'Well,' I said, 'you certainly are in lots of trouble. I'm not going to be able to help you much after today. I'm going to

Europe soon. But I'll do what I can. Enjoy yourself at Crystal Lake – try to catch some big fish!'

When I got back to my office, I rang my friend Hank. Hank works for the phone company.

'This is Len,' I said. 'Can you give me some help, Hank? Will you check this phone number on your computer? I want to know whose number it is.'

I gave Hank the number Mary Sullivan had given Mike. Then I waited while he checked his computer.

'I've got it,' Hank said, a minute later. 'It's the private office of Senator Theo Z. Democrates. I have an address for the office.'

I noted down the address and I thanked Hank. This was interesting news! Theo Democrates was the senator Toni had told me about – the man who might have been involved with Gail.

I put down the phone and it started to ring almost immediately. I answered it. It was Rik.

'Lenny, hi, how are things?'

'Rik! Has something happened to Gail?' I asked.

'No, don't worry,' Rik said quickly. 'The movie's going well now, and we're getting ready to leave for Istanbul the day after tomorrow. I want you to join us there. That's why I'm calling you. I've spoken to Mr Frank about you. Go to the Magic Movie Productions studios now. Go to the main office. Mr Frank's secretary will give you an envelope. In it, you'll find an air ticket and some instructions. A make-up artist and someone from the costume department are already in Istanbul, and they will know what to do with you.'

'But Rik,' I said. I was puzzled. 'What do you mean? Why do I need to see costume and make-up people? I'm not an actor.'

'You're going to be Brent Foster's double!' Rik replied. 'You look and sound a lot like him. When you're made up, people will think you are him!'

14

A New Man

I left my office and drove to the Magic Movie Productions studios. I asked for Mr Frank's office at Gate Four and was sent to a large administration building. I waited, and after ten minutes, I was taken to Mr Frank's office. I had expected to talk to a secretary, but I was taken in to see Mr Frank himself.

Homer Frank was a tall, bald man with a neat grey beard. He walked round his huge desk to shake my hand.

'Make yourself comfortable[2],' he said pointing to some leather armchairs in one corner of the enormous office. 'I wanted to see you myself before you left for Istanbul. Your air ticket and Rik's instructions are in this.'

He handed me a long, thin brown envelope.

'I hope that Rik has told you how important it is for this studio that nobody hurts Gail. *Death Behind the Door* is going to be a blockbuster[1] and nothing must stop us finishing it. And it's important that Gail shouldn't know anything about the threats. She would worry and that would upset her. Then she wouldn't act well.'

'I think she's already worried,' I replied, and I told Mr Frank about the attack on Gail in the Recoleta Cemetery.

'Yes, I know about that,' the studio boss replied. 'Rik called me soon after it happened. And before that, there was Josie's accident.'

'Yeah! Josie's accident! There's one thing I wanted to ask you, Mr Frank,' I said. 'Rik told me that you had received the death threats against Gail by e-mail.'

'That's correct,' Frank said.

'I don't know a lot about computers,' I went on. 'But isn't the address of the sender usually given on an e-mail message?

Where did the messages come from?'

Homer Frank looked out of the window as he answered. 'I don't know,' he replied quickly. 'When I switched on my computer, the messages were waiting for me. But there was no sender's address.'

'Could I see the messages? There might be some clues in them,' I said.

Frank shook his head. 'No, I'm afraid I deleted[4] the messages after I read them.'

Just then, a secretary came into the room. 'Excuse me, Mr Frank,' he said, 'but there's an urgent phone call for you.'

'Who is it?' Frank asked.

'The caller wouldn't give his name. It's a man, and he says he's a friend of Vincent,' the secretary replied. Then he left the room.

Homer Frank's face suddenly looked much older. He walked across to his desk and picked up a red phone. Then he sat on the desk with his back towards me. It was a short phone call. Frank said 'yes' three times and 'no' twice. Then he put the phone down and sat still and silent. After a minute, he got up and walked back to the corner where I was sitting.

'You'll have to excuse me, Samuel,' he said abruptly. 'There's some urgent work which I must do. Go to Istanbul and make sure that nothing bad happens to Gail.'

I left the administration building and got into my Chrysler. I sat and thought for a while before looking in the envelope I had in my hand. My conversation with Homer Frank had been a waste of time, but I still had a job to do. And something was wrong about those e-mail messages. Had Frank really received them? Had he lied about them? And who was the friend of Vincent whose phone call had upset Frank so badly?

Finally, I opened the envelope. It contained an American Airlines ticket to New York and a Turkish Airlines ticket from New York to Istanbul. The American Airlines flight was going to leave at nine o'clock that night! I looked at my watch. It was nearly five o'clock. I drove quickly back to my apartment, packed my bag, and took a cab to L.A. International Airport.

Soon, I was sitting in the departure lounge, reading Rik's instructions.

On arrival at Atatürk Airport, take a cab to the Swissotel. Rooms for the whole movie crew have been booked there. We will all arrive the next day on a direct flight from Buenos Aires. At the Swissotel, contact Julie Grant, the make-up artist, and Steve Tovich, from the costume department. They know what to do. The plane tickets are in your name, but your hotel room is booked in the name of Alan Davies. That will be your name in Istanbul.

—

I caught the Turkish Airlines flight in New York, and I enjoyed my first Turkish meal as we flew over the Atlantic. I hadn't visited Europe for ten years, and this was going to be my first visit to Turkey. I was looking forward to exploring Istanbul, and I read a guidebook during the flight to prepare myself.

There were long lines of passengers at the Immigration desks when we landed at Atatürk Airport. Several planes must have landed at the same time, and it took me an hour to reach a polite immigration official, who quickly put a stamp in my passport.

After that bad start, everything got better and better. It was late afternoon and the weather was very warm. The cab driver who took me to the hotel was friendly, and he pointed out the sights on the way.

The Swissotel was amazing. It was a huge building with wonderful views over the Bosphorus – the channel which divides Europe from Asia. The water was full of ships and boats of all kinds.

I checked in and found a message from Julie Grant waiting for me.

You must be very tired. Get a good night's sleep and call me in the morning. I'm in room 1012.

'Good advice!' I thought.

I had a shower, and then a fine dinner in a splendid dining-room. My table was near one of the huge windows. Night was falling, and the Bosphorus was covered with little moving points of light. It was very beautiful.

After dinner, I went for a walk in the hotel grounds. But at ten o'clock, I was ready for bed.

—

I slept for twelve hours, and when I woke, I was a new man. After breakfast, I called room 1012.

Julie Grant and Steve Tovich came to see me in my room almost immediately. Julie had a box containing make-up and Steve was carrying a bag of clothes.

'I don't know how you're going to do this,' I said as Julie opened her box. 'Brent is five years younger than me, and at least twenty kilos heavier!'

'Also he's got blue eyes and short straight blond hair,' Julie replied. 'No problem. Just relax, and you'll soon see what we can do.'

'But the make-up isn't just for a scene in the movie,' I went on nervously. 'I'm going to have to look like Brent for several days, because I mustn't look like me!'

'Relax!' Steve said. 'There's no problem.'

So I relaxed. First of all Julie washed my hair. Then she bleached it and dyed[4] it, so that it looked blond. Next, she cut it in Brent's style. After that, she changed the shape of my eyebrows and put a pair of blue contact lenses[4] into my eyes. Lastly, she put a layer of latex[1] on the lower part of my face, to make it look wider.

'You can have a shower and wash your hair without changing any of this,' Julie said. Then she started to work with brushes and paints to make my face look like Brent's.

After Julie had finished, it was Steve's turn. He fastened

She put a layer of latex on the lower part of my face.

some padding[4] around my chest to make my body look fatter, then he took some clothes out of his bag. They were the kind of clothes Brent wore, he told me. There were lots of them. I put some of them on.

'Amazing!' I said as I looked in the mirror. Both Julie and Steve clapped their hands and smiled.

'Now,' Julie said as they were getting ready to leave, 'the flight from Buenos Aires arrives later this afternoon. I suggest that you spend the next few hours getting used to your "new self". Here's a video containing scenes from some of Brent's movies. Watch it, then try to move and talk like him.'

They left, and I looked at myself in the mirror. I was Brent Foster. It was incredible!

—

At four o'clock, the phone rang. It was Gail Lane.

'Lenny, I'm in the hotel. And I've had another message!' she said.

15

Topkapi

'Gail!' I said. 'How do you know my room number? I'm called Alan Davies here.'

'Rik told me about his plan, Lenny,' Gail replied. 'I'm so happy that you're working on the movie again.'

'Wait until you see me,' I said.

'I want to see you now,' Gail said. 'I want to show you this message. It was waiting for me here, at the hotel.'

I thought carefully. This was the time to find out what Gail thought about my new self.

'I'm going down to reception for a few minutes,' I said. 'If you don't find me there, come up to my room in fifteen minutes.'

'OK, Lenny. I'll see you,' Gail said, and she hung up.

I took the elevator down to reception and I sat in a corner seat. I picked up a newspaper. Gail soon appeared and she took a seat by one of the tall windows. I put down my newspaper and walked across to her. She looked at me in surprise. Then she smiled.

'Brent, my dear, are you feeling better?' she asked.

I smiled back, and nodded my head.

'I'm so pleased,' Gail went on. 'You had such a terrible headache on the plane.'

I smiled again, waved and walked over to the elevator.

The make-up was great! I now looked so much like Brent that his co-star couldn't see that I was really Lenny Samuel!

I went back to my room. After ten minutes, there was a knock at the door.

'Come in!' I shouted. I tried to sound like Brent.

Gail came into the room, then stopped.

'What are you doing here?' she said. 'I thought this was Lenny's – I mean Alan Davies' room.'

I smiled, stood up and kissed her cheek.

'Hi, Gail,' I said in my own voice.

'Lenny!' Gail said. 'That make-up is fantastic! I saw Brent ten minutes ago in reception, you look just like him.'

'That was me in reception,' I replied with a smile. 'Please sit down, Gail.'

She immediately became serious again. 'This was waiting for me when I arrived,' she said, and she handed me a small white envelope. The Swissotel address was printed on the envelope and the message inside it was written on Swissotel notepaper.

'It's just like the message in Buenos Aires,' I thought. 'That was on Alvear Palace notepaper.'

Welcome to Istanbul, Miss Lane, I read. *You waited at the Café Pernambuco in Buenos Aires. That showed that you could be trusted. You can have the photos on your return to California. But you will have to pay $250 000 for them. I will contact you again in L.A.*

I gave the message back to Gail.

'I'm very worried,' she said. 'I'm not worried about the money. I can afford to pay. But if I pay for these photos now, how will I know there are no more copies of them?'

'You won't! And I'm sure there are,' I said. 'But this is one problem that can wait until we get back to L.A. When this person contacts you again, I'll be around to find out who the blackmailer is.'

'You're wonderful, Lenny,' Gail said with a little smile.

I didn't say anything. Gail went to her room to get some rest.

Soon, my phone rang again. This time, it was Rik. He said he was on his way up to see me.

—

'Wow!' Rik said, a few minutes later. 'Julie and Steve did a great job. You too, Len! You look and sound just like Brent! Now, let me tell you what's going to happen tomorrow. We're shooting at the Topkapi Palace. It would be good if you visited the area by yourself today. Look around the outside of the palace, and explore the streets which lead to it.

'You're going to be Brent's double. Tomorrow, you'll have no problems getting onto the set. I've arranged a pass for you in the name of Alan Davies. All you've got to do tomorrow is to sit and watch the shooting. Then, very early the next day, we'll shoot the last outdoor scenes here in Turkey. First, we'll shoot the scene in which you'll be Brent's double. In that scene, Brent and Gail are together, and Brent drives Gail away from the palace in a Ford Mustang.'

'Not many people know this,' Rik went on. 'But Brent can't drive a car. He's frightened of cars! So you'll act in the first part of the car chase[1] instead of Brent.'

'What do you mean by "car chase", Rik?' I asked.

'Yeah, well – when Brent drives Gail away in the Mustang, another car follows it down the hill, towards the Golden Horn. Later on, we'll shoot a real car chase through Istanbul – we don't need the stars to be involved in that. We'll use stunt-doubles dressed like the movie actors. But the first part – the escape from Topkapi – has to be shot in close-up. It has to look real,' Rik explained. 'So you and Gail will be in the car. All you have to do is to drive quite quickly down the hill. The Mercedes containing the bad guys will follow you.'

'That sounds easy,' I replied.

Then I asked Rik about the last couple of days of shooting in B.A.

'No problems,' Rik said. 'There was one strange thing, though. At Ezeiza Airport, an Argentine police captain called Garcia spoke to me. He said that he had been keeping an eye on Gail too. Do you know anything about that, Len? Who's Garcia?'

'A friend of mine,' I said with a smile. 'I'm glad to hear that nothing bad happened.'

'Arabella and Annie still believe that you were involved in the attack at the Recoleta Cemetery,' Rik added. 'I hope they don't recognize you in this make-up. They will make a lot of trouble if they do! Gail is the only other person who knows that Alan Davies is really Lenny Samuel.'

Soon, Rik said goodbye and went off to get some sleep. I took a cab to the Topkapi Palace. I had my guidebook with me, but I didn't read it. I looked out of the window of the cab at the fascinating city of Istanbul. I had read enough to know that the Topkapi Palace was over five hundred years old. When I got there, I discovered that the palace was much, much bigger than I had thought it was. The guidebook said that the four magnificent courtyards and the surrounding buildings had once been the home of more than five thousand people. It was going to be difficult to protect Gail in such a large area.

I spent an hour walking around the outside of the palace. There was no time to go into any of the beautiful buildings that day. I tried to remember which streets led away from the gateway, down to the Golden Horn. Standing outside the palace entrance, I looked out over the Bosphorus and the Sea of Marmara, and then down the hill to Sultanahmet Square and Aya Sofia.

I walked down to Aya Sofia and looked at that magnificent building, which was more than fifteen hundred years old. First it had been a church, and then a mosque, but now it was a museum. It was stunning.

I walked for a while among the crowds of people in the streets. I liked Istanbul, though it was as different from L.A. as anything could be! At last, I waved for a cab and rode back to the hotel. I was excited about the next couple of days. Pretending to be a movie star was going to be fun!

I walked for a while among the crowds of people in the streets.

16

Mustang and Mercedes

At six o'clock the next morning, buses took the technicians, extras, and most of the other people who were needed that day, to the Topkapi Palace. There, a hundred Turkish workers were waiting for us, and the crew started to prepare the sound system, the lighting and the cameras. A row of trailers was parked outside the palace. These were the mobile dressing-rooms and the make-up department. Soon, dozens of policemen were needed to keep the crowd away from the crew. Even at this early hour, many people wanted to watch what was happening. As it was a Tuesday, the palace itself was closed to visitors all day.

The crowd became excited at seven o'clock, when Gail and Brent arrived in a long black limousine. Carla was already on the set, working with the lighting cameraman[1]. I was just leaving one of the make-up trailers when the two stars arrived. Julie Grant had been repairing my make-up. I wasn't needed for that day's shooting, but Carla wanted to see me standing next to Brent. She wanted to check that we looked the same. Carla thought that I was a double called Alan Davies, of course, and I wanted her to go on believing that!

'Hey, man!' a voice said and I felt a hand on my shoulder. I turned around and saw that it was the real Brent Foster.

'Well, I just can't believe this!' Brent said as he looked at me. 'I've had lots of doubles in my time, but none of them looked as good as you.' He held out his hand.

I took his hand and shook it. 'The name's Davies – Alan Davies,' I said. 'It's a great pleasure to meet you.'

At that moment, Carla came over and looked at the two of us carefully. For a few seconds, I was worried.

'Wonderful!' she said. 'Which of you is the double?'

'I'll see you later, Alan,' Brent said, and walked off towards his dressing-room.

—

The morning passed slowly. Carla was shooting some outdoor scenes of Gail and Brent running through the courts of the Topkapi, being chased by two men in red T-shirts. I wasn't in any of the scenes. I didn't think Gail was in any danger that morning. Arabella and Annie were with her when she wasn't on the set. I was pleased that neither of them recognized me.

I had never really found out what the story of the movie was, so I asked Julie about it.

'I don't know either,' she replied. 'None of us knows really, not even the actors. That's Carla's way of working – she shoots lots of scenes and then puts the story together during editing, back at the studios in L.A.'

'I see,' I said, although I really didn't understand at all. 'But the actors must know who they are playing. For example – the two men in red T-shirts. What parts are they playing?'

'They're the bad guys in the movie,' Julie replied. 'Brent is playing a criminal, but he isn't a real bad guy! The men in T-shirts are playing New York gangsters, I do know that. But I'm not sure why they're chasing Brent and Gail in this scene.'

'Well, thanks,' I said and went and sat down in a cool part of the courtyard. The sun was getting hotter. By midday, it was very hot indeed.

In the late afternoon, I watched the technicians lay the metal rails for the camera to run on. This was near the Imperial Gate, the main entrance to the palace. Gail and Brent were going to run across the courtyard and out through the gate. Then shooting would stop for the day. Very early the next morning, we would start again. This time it would be Gail and me running out of the Imperial Gate and getting into the Ford Mustang. I was going to be in a movie! I was so excited, I could hardly sleep that night.

—

I needn't have got so excited. We arrived at the set at four o'clock the next morning. We had to shoot the scene before there was much traffic on the roads. It took nearly an hour to get the cameras and lights in the right positions. Then Carla asked Gail and me to rehearse[1] our scene. We had to run out of the gate and get into the car. Who would have thought that a simple thing like getting into a car could be so difficult? Carla made us do it again and again. Then she shot the scene three times. Each time, she changed the position of the cameras.

After that, she did some shots of me closing the car door and starting the engine. I had to do this several times too.

'OK, Alan,' Carla said as she put her head in through the car window. 'That was fine. Now I want you to start the car and drive away. Remember, you are being chased. I want a real fast start! Spin the car wheels! As you start the car, the two guys in red will come running out of the gate and they will reach the car just as you drive off. Then they'll get into the Mercedes and follow you.'

'We'll be behind both cars in these.' Carla pointed to two trucks with cameras on them. 'Just go down the hill as far as the tramlines[4], but don't let the Mercedes catch you,' she said. 'It'll be easy! OK?'

'I hope so,' I said with a nervous smile.

When Carla walked away, Gail touched my arm. 'Don't worry, Lenny. You'll be fine,' she said.

It wasn't as easy as Carla had said. The first time I tried to do a high-speed start, the car's engine stopped. The second time, I spun the wheels so much that a cloud of smoke and dust came up from the ground. The cameramen couldn't see us. The third time I started too quickly, and the guys in red couldn't reach our car before we drove away.

Carla was very patient. 'OK, let's do it once more,' she said with a smile.

'Cameras! Action!'

I tried again. This time it was good! The Mustang shot forward as the two men in red shirts came running out of the Imperial Gate. They just reached the Mustang as we drove away, with our wheels spinning and our tyres screaming. Then they jumped into a black Mercedes which was waiting with its engine running[4].

I looked in the driving-mirror as I drove away from the Topkapi Palace. The Mercedes was just swinging out behind us. Behind the Mercedes were the two trucks with cameras on them.

I felt great. We had done it! I looked at Gail. The windows were open and her hair was blowing in the wind. She looked beautiful!

'Watch the road, Lenny,' Gail said. 'And stop looking at me.' But she laughed.

We were outside the palace area now and, although it was only half-past five, there was quite a lot of traffic on the road. I had to go slowly behind a crowded minibus, and the Mercedes got much closer to us. Looking quickly in the driving-mirror, I overtook the minibus and I put my foot down[2]. But the Mercedes continued to get closer. I put my hand on the horn. The loud sound made a group of people who were crossing the road jump out of the way.

The black Mercedes was coming closer and closer, but the camera trucks were now far behind. They couldn't get any shots from that distance. Something was wrong!

'This wasn't meant to happen,' I shouted to Gail as I swerved[4] to avoid a bus. 'Carla's going to make us do this scene again.'

Gail didn't reply. She was staring in horror at an old man, who was pushing a cart across the road in front of us. I hit the brakes. The tyres screamed! Then I put my foot down on the accelerator again and turned the steering wheel hard. We rushed past the cart, missing it by a few centimetres. But a

Then I put my foot down on the accelerator again and turned the steering wheel hard.

moment later, there was a crash as the Mercedes hit it, pushing it off the road. I looked in the mirror and I was pleased to see that the old man was OK, even if his cart wasn't.

But the Mercedes was getting close to us again, and soon it was only a few metres behind us.

Bang!

The Mercedes hit the back of the Mustang! Fortunately the road in front was clear, and I put my foot down again.

Crack! Crack!

Two gun shots! What was happening? I looked in the mirror again. The passenger in the Mercedes was leaning out of his window with a gun in his hand.

'This was definitely not meant to happen!' I shouted to Gail. 'Get down!'

'Shut up[2] and drive faster,' she replied from the floor of the car.

I pushed the accelerator to the floor.

17

The Bridge Over the Golden Horn

I looked in the driving-mirror and saw that the Mercedes had been stopped by a tram which was crossing in front of it. I slowed down a little and turned right, starting to drive back towards the centre of the city. I thought that if we were in a crowded place, the passenger in the Mercedes wouldn't use his gun again. I hadn't even started to think about who these people were, or why they were trying to kill us.

I tried hard to remember the map from my guidebook. The Mustang raced through the narrow streets towards the railway station. There were more people here and I used the horn all the time. This didn't help very much, as all the other drivers were doing the same. Everybody does it in Istanbul!

Then I saw some water between two buildings, and realized where we were. We were near the pier[4] where all the Bosphorus ferries start their journeys.

Crack!

Another shot. I'd guessed that the man in the Mercedes wouldn't use his gun in crowded places. It wasn't a very good guess!

I looked down at Gail, who was sitting on the floor of the car – the safest place to be. I drove the Mustang through the crowds and came out on to a wider road by the side of the Bosphorus – the road which led to the wide Galata Bridge.

The Galata Bridge crosses the part of the Bosphorus which is called the Golden Horn. As we got near the bridge, I looked in the driving-mirror and saw that the Mercedes was very close to us again. But I also saw another car – a small blue Fiat. It was right behind the Mercedes, and going very fast.

'Oh no!' I thought. 'There are two cars chasing us now.'

Ahead of me, a traffic light changed to red. I closed my eyes and put my foot down hard. We crossed the junction safely. Behind us, the Mercedes and the Fiat were stopped by the buses and trucks crossing in the other direction. I told Gail it was safe to get up, and I was pleased to see how calm she was.

Out of the corner of my eye[2], I saw a broken metal barrier[4]. There was another red light, but I didn't stop. In a moment, we were driving onto the bridge. We could see the Galata Tower on the other side of the Golden Horn. If we could get out of the car on the other side of the bridge, we could run into the narrow streets near the tower. We could escape the gunman.

But suddenly, the Mercedes was a hundred metres behind us again, following us onto the bridge. I heard the noise of a siren.

'Good!' I thought. 'The police are coming.'

We were on the wide bridge, with the blue water beneath us. In one minute we would be safe! But then I looked in the mirror and I saw the Mercedes, right behind us again. And the blue Fiat was still behind the Mercedes.

Crack!

There was another shot and Gail got down onto the floor again. Sooner or later, one of these bullets was going to hit us. I decided the time had come to fight back. The bridge was wide and there wasn't any other traffic on it. That was very strange, but it was useful! I braked hard, very suddenly. I pulled the steering wheel round and, using the handbrake[4], I turned the car right around. Now we were facing the Mercedes. I put my foot on the accelerator and I drove straight at it. The driver of the Mercedes tried to swerve to avoid a crash.

The Mustang and Mercedes just touched each other, but that was enough! The Mercedes skidded[4] sideways and the blue Fiat, which was right behind it, crashed into it.

I turned the Mustang round again and started to drive back over the bridge. But suddenly, the car was going slower and slower. It was like climbing up a steep hill. And the view ahead was changing. I couldn't see the Galata Tower any more – only sky! Then I realized what was happening. The Galata Bridge was opening!

The Galata Bridge is made in two halves – it can open in the middle. Each half of the bridge can swing upwards, so that big ships can pass along the Golden Horn. And the bridge was opening now, and we were driving towards the gap in the middle! We were going to drop off one end of the roadway, into the water below.

I hit the brakes. The tyres screamed and we stopped right on the end of our half of the bridge.

'Are you OK?' I asked Gail who was still on the floor.

'Fine,' she replied. 'Let's get out of here!'

She got up onto her seat. 'What the hell!' she said, when she saw where we were.

A moment later, Gail opened her door. Then she screamed.

'There's just water below me, Lenny,' she said. 'I can't get out of the car!'

'I think we can both get out on my side,' I replied quickly. 'We must try, before the car falls into the water.'

I started to open my door and started to get out, but as I moved, the car started to tip forward. The Mustang was balanced right on the end of the roadway. Every time I moved, the car moved too. We were trapped in the car.

Then we looked at what was happening behind us. Two men in dark suits had got out of the blue Fiat and they had taken charge. They had pulled the driver and the passenger out of the Mercedes, and they had taken the passenger's gun. Now, one of the men from the Fiat was guarding the two men in red T-shirts, and the other was talking into a mobile phone.

The man with the phone looked at our car. He said something to his partner and he started to climb up the bridge towards us. He had to crawl forward on his hands and knees.

He stopped when he saw that the Mustang was balanced on

*'There's just water below me, Lenny.
I can't get out of the car!'*

the end of the bridge. He was still a few metres away from us, but I could see that he was about thirty, a handsome man with bright eyes.

'You must be Miss Lane,' he said to Gail. 'I'm Sergeant Kamal of the Istanbul police. Your embassy asked me to make sure that nobody hurt you while you were in our city.'

Then he looked at me. 'Why did you drive onto the bridge, sir?' he asked. 'I know the barrier is broken. But didn't you see the red light? Didn't you hear the siren which sounds when the bridge is going to open?'

I didn't know what to say, so I just smiled.

'Well, don't move,' Sergeant Kamal said. 'We'll soon get you down from here.'

He needn't have worried. We weren't going to move!

I watched the sergeant crawl back down towards the bridge entrance. Lots of traffic was stopped there. And a large crowd of people was standing and watching us. I wondered what Sergeant Kamal was going to do. It would be impossible to bring a truck or a crane up the steep slope of the bridge.

Gail and I sat and waited. Then suddenly, she started to talk to me. She talked quickly and seriously.

'Lenny,' she began. 'I haven't told you all of the truth about myself. There's something you ought to know.'

18

Gail's Story

Gail and I sat in the Mustang, hanging over the end of the Galata Bridge, above the blue waters of the Golden Horn.

'There's someone I must tell you about,' Gail said. 'You already know about the photos of me dancing with Vincent Calab. Well, he's not the only man I've been involved with. There have been two others. One of them is Mike Devine. I've been going out with him for several years, but he's really only a friend. I don't see him very often any more.'

'Because he started to borrow money from you?' I guessed.

Gail looked at me in surprise. 'How did you know?' she asked.

I smiled. 'Mike told me that he'd been borrowing money from everyone he knew. I guessed that included you,' I replied.

'Mike's a nice guy when he isn't drinking,' Gail said. 'But when he drinks too much, he's an enemy to himself.'

'He has other enemies too,' I said.

'What do you mean, Lenny?' Gail asked.

I told her about my meeting with Mike Devine in L.A. I told her that I had lent him my cabin in Crystal Lake. I told her about Mary Sullivan.

Gail was silent for a minute. 'Mmm,' she said. 'Having to leave L.A. is probably the best thing that could happen to Mike.'

'Who do you think Miss Sullivan is working for?' I asked.

'I don't know,' Gail replied. 'What do *you* think?'

'Well, she told Mike to leave L.A. But she also told him not to see you again, Gail,' I said. 'That's very interesting, isn't it?'

Gail sighed but she didn't say anything.

'I think Miss Sullivan works for someone who's very

important,' I said. 'Someone with enough power to order men from the US Embassy in Buenos Aires to follow you. Someone with enough power to ask the Turkish police to protect you. Sergeant Kamal isn't an ordinary policeman, Gail. Can you think who this person might be?'

Gail looked out over the blue water. 'I said there was something I wanted to tell you,' she said. 'I said I had been involved with two other men. Please listen a minute and stop asking me questions.

'There is someone important in my life,' she went on. 'He's someone I've known for about eighteen months. We are engaged to be married, but it's still a secret. You're right, he's a very powerful man, but he's also a very jealous one. He's a politician and he's afraid that if there's any scandal[4] about us, he won't be elected.'

'Wait a minute,' I said. 'If we are talking about Senator Democrates, he's already *been* elected. So what's the problem?'

'How did you know I was talking about Theo?' Gail asked. 'Never mind – you're right, Lenny. It is Theo Democrates. He's been elected to the Senate, of course. But he wants to be the next President. When I first met you, I thought you were one of the people he pays to look after me.'

I shook my head. 'No,' I replied. 'It's true that I'm here to protect you, but Magic Movie Productions hired me, not Senator Democrates.'

'The studio? Why did the studio hire *you?*' Gail asked. 'The studio hired Arabella and Annie as my bodyguards.'

I decided to tell Gail the truth. She knew now that someone was trying to kill her. I told her that Homer Frank had received messages, which threatened her life.

'I understand. I know this movie is very important for the studio,' Gail said. Then she sat silently for a few minutes.

Time passed. The Mustang moved gently whenever one of us moved. The crowd of people at the entrance to the bridge stood and stared at us.

Then I heard the sound of a large engine in the distance. It was coming closer. Was it a ship, moving towards the bridge? I was worried, but Gail seemed not to hear the noise.

Suddenly, Sergeant Kamal crawled up to the Mustang again and told us that help was coming soon.

'Please sit still and do nothing,' he said and crawled back towards the crowd.

'There's something else, Lenny,' Gail said. 'I told you that I hadn't been in contact with Vincent Calab for years. That's not true. He called me a couple of weeks ago.'

'What did he say?' I asked.

'It wasn't what he said that scared me,' Gail replied. 'It was how he said it. He was horrible! He sounded completely mad. The message was very simple. He said that if I didn't want to get hurt, I should stop working on *Death Behind the Door.* He didn't explain why, he just told me to leave the movie. He was giving me an order.

'And what did *you* say?' I asked.

'Well, I don't like people giving me orders. I told him that,' she answered with a quick smile. 'He started shouting so I hung up.'

'I don't expect people do that to him very often,' I said. 'But we need to know why Calab wants to stop the movie. And I'm sure we'll find the answer to that question back in Hollywood.'

The sound of the engine I had heard was getting louder and louder.

'What's that noise?' Gail asked suddenly.

We both tried to look out of the car, but our movements made the Mustang move, so we sat still again. Then Sergeant Kamal and another policeman came crawling up towards us with two long chains in their arms. The engine noise was very loud now, and suddenly there was a great shadow over the car. We could not look up.

The two policemen seemed to be fastening the chains to the back wheels of the Mustang. Then the sergeant fixed the chains together over the car's roof.

The noise got even louder, and suddenly a great hook came down from the sky. Had someone found a crane that could reach us? I couldn't see one.

The Mustang started to move! The back of the car started to rise. But the Mustang was moving forwards, further over the end of the bridge. I held Gail's arm.

'Oh no,' I said. 'We're going to fall.'

With a noise like a scream, the Mustang slid slowly off the end of the bridge and it started to fall towards the blue sea. Then suddenly, we stopped falling and we were swinging slowly from side to side. A moment later, we were moving upwards! Gail and I looked at each other in amazement.

'I must be dreaming,' Gail said.

I leant out of the window and looked up. Above us were the two giant rotors[4] of a Chinook helicopter. I looked down and saw the Galata Bridge far below us.

'You're not dreaming,' I said to Gail with a laugh. 'We're flying.'

Above us were the two giant rotors of a Chinook helicopter.

19

Hollywood Again

The Turkish Air Force Chinook did not carry the Mustang very far. It carried the car carefully to the road near the bridge entrance. First the front wheels touched the ground, then the back wheels were gently lowered. Two policemen quickly removed the chains from the hook, and the helicopter flew away.

'What a pity the flight was so short,' Gail said. 'I wanted to see Istanbul from the air.'

Sergeant Kamal was waiting for us when we got out of the car.

'You're wonderful,' Gail said to him. 'You saved our lives. I don't know how to thank you.'

Sergeant Kamal smiled. 'The two men who were chasing you in the Mercedes were Americans,' he said. 'But they weren't members of your movie crew. I've been talking to your director, Miss Chapman, at Topkapi Palace. The two men who should have been in the car have been found near the Imperial Gate. They were unconscious. They had both been hit on the head and tied up. But they are OK now. The men who chased you are being questioned at Police Headquarters, so we'll soon know who they are working for.'

The sergeant took us back to the movie set in a police car. Carla Chapman was waiting for us.

'Are you both OK?' she asked. 'We were so worried! You drove away from the palace so fast. It must have been terrifying!'

Gail told Carla about our adventure on the Galata Bridge and about the helicopter. Carla was shocked when she heard about the danger to the star of her movie.

'Still, there's one good thing,' Carla said with a smile. 'We got some really good shots of the car chase before you got too far from the cameras. What a pity we couldn't shoot you on the bridge!'

It wasn't possible to shoot any more scenes that day, so we all went back to the hotel. So there were still two more days of shooting to be done before we all went back to Hollywood. I wasn't needed as Brent's double any longer, but I had to go on being Alan Davies, of course. I went to watch the shooting on both days. I had plenty of time to think about Gail's problems.

On the second day, I made two decisions. The first was to go on using my Brent Foster clothes and make-up for a few days *after* we returned to L.A. The second was to send a fax to Homer Frank from Brent, asking for an appointment to see him.

'We'll go and see Frank together,' I explained to Gail, 'and we'll find out what he really knows about these threats. But I'll go as Brent, not as myself!'

So the morning after the long flight back from Istanbul, Gail and I drove to Gate Four of the Magic Movie Productions studios in Hollywood. Gail was looking beautiful, and I was still pretending to be Brent Foster. I was 'wired for sound'. I had a microphone hidden in my clothes. It would transmit[4] to a tape recorder in my car. Every word that anyone near me said would be recorded.

The security guards at the gate took one look at us and let us through. We were big stars! We didn't have to wait at the entrance to the administration building either. We were taken straight into Homer Frank's huge office.

'Gail!' Frank said. 'It's good to see you! I was only expecting[2] Brent. It's a real surprise to see you too!'

It was to be a morning of surprises. The real Brent Foster got a surprise too, though I only heard about it the next day. He also came to the studios that morning. But the security guards stopped him at the gate. They wouldn't let him in. They had already seen me go in with Gail, so they thought Brent was someone *pretending* to be Brent Foster.

We got several surprises too. Our first surprise came a few minutes after we had sat down in the leather chairs in Frank's office. The office door opened, and Frank's secretary came in with his hands above his head. He was followed by Annie and Arabella with their hands above *their* heads. They were followed by two short men in long black jackets, carrying long black guns. And they were followed by a slim man in his fifties with shiny black hair. He was wearing a beautiful suit.

I looked at Gail.

'I told Arabella and Annie we'd be here,' she said quietly. 'You can guess who the others are.'

Vincent Calab, the man in the beautiful suit, stopped in surprise when he saw Gail. Then he walked over to her, took her hand, and kissed it.

'What the hell is going on?' Homer Frank asked in a high, frightened voice. 'Who are you? We've never met.'

'I'm sorry, sir,' the secretary said. 'This man told me that you were expecting him. I knew you weren't and I told him you were busy, but he wouldn't listen to me.'

'That's right – that's how I am,' Calab said with a thin, nasty smile. 'I never listen to anyone. I give the orders. All I wanted was a little help from Gail here. Gail, who I helped so much in the past.'

The gangster's voice rose suddenly from a whisper to a scream. 'And what did she say to me? "No", is what she said. Was I going to take that? No, I wasn't!'

He looked around the room wildly.

Gail said to him. 'Why have you been trying to kill me, Vincent?'

'You know why,' Calab replied. 'You're still alive, though. You're still alive because of a private eye. A private eye who I'm still trying to find.'

Then Calab turned to me.

'Mr Foster. I'm pleased to meet you, sir.'

I didn't say anything. Calab didn't know that the private eye had driven Gail's car as Brent's double. Now, like Homer Frank, he thought I really was Brent. But I was worried about Calab. He was very dangerous. One minute he was calm and sane, the next minute he was a madman.

'You say that we've never met,' Calab said to Homer Frank. 'And that is true. But you've taken a lot of my money, haven't you? I've invested over one billion[4] dollars in your stupid little studios. I'm the person who's been paying your bills. And now, you have a movie that's going to be a big success, I expected to get all my money back. I've asked for it. But you tell me that you won't give my money back. You say that there's no evidence that I gave you any money.'

Calab's voice had been calm and quiet while he spoke to the chief executive. But now it rose to a scream again.

'No! Of course there isn't any evidence. That was our arrangement. There musn't be any evidence! I gave you the dirty money so you could give it back to me clean.'

Then the gangster was calm again.

'So, you refuse to give me my money?' he said. 'Very well, I'll make sure that *Death Behind the Door* is never finished. With Gail Lane dead, your studio will have no future. If you don't agree to pay me the money now, I will kill your star!'

'Just wait a minute,' I said quickly. I was angry and I forgot to speak like Brent Foster. 'I'm only a stupid actor, and there are some things that I don't understand. Let's start with Josie – why did you injure her?'

'We wanted to frighten Miss Lane,' Calab replied. 'That was a good way to do it.'

'And the stone ball in the cemetery in Buenos Aires?' I asked. 'Was that one of your tricks too?'

'Yes, that was a good trick, wasn't it?' Calab smiled. 'One of

*'If you don't agree to pay me the money now,
I will kill your star.'*

my men hid in the cemetery overnight. He was painted white, and when you all arrived, he stood on the roof with the stone ball. But we were still only trying to frighten Miss Lane. The ball would have missed her.'

'Well, I know you weren't just trying to frighten Gail in Istanbul,' I said, 'because I was in the car with her. Your men were trying to kill us.'

Calab smiled his thin smile again. 'Enough of your stupid questions!' he shouted. 'Of course I wanted to kill her. With Miss Lane dead, the movie couldn't be finished.'

'Hey, boss,' one of the gunmen said to Calab. 'There's something wrong here. I go to the movies a lot and I've seen all of Brent Foster's movies. This guy looks like Brent, but he doesn't talk like him. Are you sure he's really Foster?'

Calab walked up to me and looked closely at my face. Then he quickly pulled off the layer of latex, and scratched away some of my make-up with his fingernails.

'So,' Calab said. He was pleased. His voice was quiet but very dangerous. 'We've found the private eye now.' He turned to Frank. 'Will you pay me my money?'

Homer Frank shook his head.

Calab turned to his men. 'OK, shoot Miss Lane,' he screamed.

Then lots of things happened very quickly. Arabella and Annie were flying through the air at the two heavies with guns. The women kicked the guns from the heavies' hands. At the same moment, I jumped forward at Calab. But suddenly, there was a small gun in *his* hand.

I grabbed Calab's arm as he fired the gun. The bullet missed me but I heard a scream from the other side of the room. I pushed Calab's arm behind his back. He was a strong man, and he fought wildly, like an animal.

I looked over Calab's shoulder. 'In here, Lieutenant,' I shouted.

It was an old trick, but the gangster was so angry that he fell for it[2]. As he looked round, I kicked his legs and let go of his arm. As he fell, I kicked him hard on the side of his head.

I picked up Calab's gun and looked around. Arabella and Annie had won their fight with the two heavies and had taken their guns. Gail and the secretary were OK, but there was blood on Homer Frank's shoulder. Calab's bullet had hit him. He was in a lot of pain, but he would live!

I walked over to the desk and picked up the phone.

'Get me the L.A.P.D.,' I said. 'I want to speak to Lieutenant Dickinson.'

—

Gail and I spent the rest of the day at the studios with Dickinson. I told him about my hidden microphone. The lieutenant listened to the tape recording of what had happened in Frank's office.

'What do you think will happen to Homer, and Vincent and his men?' Gail asked me as we finally left the office.

'Vincent Calab will get himself a good lawyer, but his words are on the tape,' I replied. 'And his words on the tape will send him to jail. It'll probably take months to find out if Homer Frank has really been laundering Calab's money.'

Soon, I said goodbye as Gail drove off with Arabella and Annie. I went to try and find Rik. My job was over and I wanted to get paid before everyone knew about Frank and Calab. However, Rik wasn't in his office. I waited for an hour. Then I left the studios and drove back to my own office.

The red light on my answerphone told me that I had some messages. There were two calls for me. I pressed the button and listened to the first one. It was Gail.

'Lenny, when I got home there was a letter for me. A letter about the photos. Please call me as soon as you can.'

20

The End

I called Gail at once.

'The letter says that I have to take the two hundred and fifty thousand dollars to the studios this afternoon at four o'clock,' Gail told me. 'I have to wait alone in the Gate Four parking lot, near the phone booth. Then I'll get another message.'

'OK,' I replied. 'Get the money and do what the letter says. I'll be there too, but you won't see me. Don't bring Arabella and Annie.'

'Are you sure, Lenny?' Gail asked anxiously. 'I'm really worried.'

'Yes, I'm sure,' I replied. 'I'll talk to you later.'

I put down the phone and I thought for a moment. Then I played the second message on the answerphone. It was Mike Devine, phoning from Crystal Lake.

'Hi, Samuel,' he said. 'I'm having a great time up here. I caught some real big fish yesterday. It's so good here, I don't even miss L.A! Thanks again for your help.'

'Well,' I thought, 'that's one satisfied client.' Although of course he hadn't paid me yet, except with a bad cheque.

I opened one of the drawers of my filing cabinet and I pulled out a phone repairman's uniform and a toolbox. Then I phoned Costas. I asked him to lend me the ladder that he keeps for working on the roof of his bar.

—

At three o'clock, I was back at the studios, dressed as a phone repairman and carrying Costas' ladder and my toolbox. I showed the security guard at Gate Four a phone company pass which I'd got from Hank. The guard let me through. I climbed up on to the roof of a low building near the parking lot, and I pretended to work on the phone lines.

Exactly at four o'clock, Gail arrived in her car. I saw her park in the far corner of the lot, near a phone booth. I took a pair of binoculars out of my tool box and I watched Gail's car. At four-fifteen, the phone in the booth rang. Gail got out of her car to answer it. She was carrying a plastic bag which I thought must contain the money. She answered the phone and listened for a moment. Then she left the booth, got back in her car and drove away. She had left the plastic bag in the booth. I waited.

Five minutes later, I saw a man walk across the parking lot to the phone booth. He had an envelope in his hand which he put on top of the phone in the booth. Then he picked up the plastic bag and walked back across the lot and into a building.

I knew who the man was.

—

At half-past four, Gail drove back into the parking lot and collected the envelope from the phone booth. Then she drove away again. I packed up my things and climbed down from the roof. It was a short walk to the building which the man had gone into. I knew this building – I had been inside it before.

I didn't knock at the office door. I just opened it and walked in.

'Hi, Rik,' I said.

'Hi, Len,' Rik replied. 'Are you working for the phone company now?' He didn't look surprised to see me.

'I wanted to tell you what's been happening,' I began. 'And I've come to collect my money, of course.'

'I don't think you're going to get paid,' Rik said with a laugh. 'Homer Frank's been arrested.'

'But, you've just been paid, Rik, haven't you?' I said calmly.

'What do you mean, Len?' Rik asked. He didn't sound happy.

'I was thinking about the time we were in the L.A.P.D.

together,' I said. 'You were investigating gangsters.'

'Yeah, that's right,' Rik said. 'I followed gangsters day and night. It was a terrible job.'

I nodded. 'And I suppose you took photos of them too,' I added.

Rik sat very still, but he didn't say anything.

'And when you left the L.A.P.D., you took some of the photos with you,' I went on. 'You thought they might be useful one day. And one day, they were very useful. It was the day when a girl you had seen dancing with a gangster became a movie star.'

Rik stared at me.

'And today you got paid – two hundred and fifty thousand bucks,' I said. 'A quarter of a million! Why did you blackmail Gail, Rik? And why did you hire me? You didn't care about Gail. I suppose you wanted to keep her alive so that you could blackmail her.'

Rik said nothing.

'We've known each other a long time, Rik,' I said. 'I'm not going to tell the police about this. Just give me the money, I'll give it back to Gail, and we'll forget all about it. I'll forget all about it unless you tell anyone you have more copies of those photos.'

Rik opened the top drawer of his desk. He took out Gail's plastic bag and gave it to me.

'I don't know what you're talking about, Len,' he said. 'But I found this bag in a phone booth in the parking lot. I'm Head of Security, so I took it. I was going to try and find out who it belonged to.'

'Sure, Rik,' I said with a smile, 'That's your story. But I know you're the blackmailer. I saw you leave the envelope with the photographs in the booth when you took the bag.'

Rik shook his head. He didn't say anything else.

I left his office and drove back to mine. I was feeling sad. I'd always liked Rik Roma.

I called Gail. She asked me to bring the bag over to her apartment immediately.

—

Gail let me into her apartment and she kissed me on the cheek. The apartment was plain but beautiful. The furniture was expensive. There was a wonderful view.

I gave Gail the plastic bag. I didn't tell her that Rik was the blackmailer. I said that I had followed a man who taken the bag from the phone booth. I said I had fought him and taken the bag from him. I said I didn't know him, and that I hadn't tried to find out who he was. And I said that if she heard from him again, she had to call me straight away.

'You are wonderful, Lenny,' Gail said. 'There's something I want to tell you, and there's someone I want you to meet. I want to tell you that I'm leaving the movie business. No more movies for me! And I want you to meet Theo, the man I'm going to marry.'

She went into another room and came back with a tall, smiling, dark-haired man.

'Hi! I'm Theo,' he said and he put his arms around Gail. 'I have to thank you for looking after Miss Lane. You're a great guy!'

Then he spoke to Gail. 'Come on, honey,' he said. 'We've got things to do.'

'OK, Theo,' she said. 'I'm coming. Goodbye, Lenny. Good luck!'

I realized that I would never see Gail again. And I wasn't going to get any money from the studio. The case was closed!

I drove back to my office and called the cabin at Crystal Lake.

'Hi! It's Lenny,' I said, when Mike Devine answered. 'I'm coming up to the cabin to do some fishing. I'll see you in a few hours.'

'Hi! I'm Theo. I have to thank you for looking after Miss Lane.'

'Well,' I said to myself as I drove out of L.A. 'No money for this case, no girl, and no career in the movies. Perhaps I'll have better luck with the fish!'

Points for Understanding

1

1 What was Lenny doing at the beginning of the story?
2 Who was Charlie?
3 Lenny, describing his Chrysler, tells the reader, 'They don't make cars like that any more.' Is he pleased about this? Why/why not?

2

1 At the beginning of the chapter, Lenny was talking to a blonde woman. He knew her name. How did he know this?
2 What did Lenny think Gail wanted him to do? Was he right?
3 Using the information contained in the first two chapters, write out Mike Devine's full address, using words for the figures.

3

1 Lenny had driven Mike Devine back to his home, but now Mike did not know who Lenny was. He thought that Lenny was an intruder. Why was this?
2 Lenny wanted to know who had hit him on the head. He had an idea, and he asked Mike a question. What was Lenny's idea? What did Mike's answer tell Lenny about his idea?

4

1 What was Crazy Ellen's? Who was Crazy Ellen?
2 What is an answerphone?
3 Why were there nuns, warriors, peasants and princesses in the studio commissary?
4 'You always were a bad liar,' Rik said to Lenny. Why does he say this?

5

1 Why do you think Lenny did not tell Rik that he really had spoken to Gail on the phone?

2 The studio's chief executive and Rik Roma had decided not to tell Gail about the death threats. Was Lenny happy about this decision? Why/why not?
3 Lenny saw a sign which said, DEATH BEHIND THE DOOR – SET CLOSED. Explain the meaning of this sign.

6

1 When Lenny walked away from the movie set, he felt terrible. Why?
2 When Rik introduced Lenny to Arabella and Annie, Arabella laughed. Why?
3 'Haven't we met before?' Gail asked Lenny. Lenny's answer was a lie. Why did he tell this lie?

7

1 Why did Rik think that Lenny would be able to find out who was threatening Gail?
2 On the plane to B.A., Lenny thought about the case. He had plenty of questions but no answers. What did he plan to do next?

8

1 Gail was being blackmailed by someone. How?
2 Did Gail have any idea about who the blackmailer was?

9

1 Excuse me, Miss Lane,' Lenny said. 'This package is for you.' Why did Lenny give Gail a package at the cemetery gateway?
2 'Was I dreaming?' Lenny had asked himself. Why did he think he might be dreaming? Was he dreaming?

10

1 Why did Lenny tell the tango dancer that it was Gail's birthday?
2 Gail did not think that the blackmailer was the person who had tried to kill her at the cemetery. Why not?

11

1 'There's something I've got to tell you,' Lenny told Rik quietly. What did Lenny want to tell Rik?
2 Rik had an idea about how to get Lenny onto the movie set in Istanbul. What was his idea? Why was this idea going to be necessary?
3 'My third call was to myself,' Lenny tells the reader. What does he mean?

12

1 Was Lenny worried about the visitors who had searched his office while he was in B.A? Why/why not?
2 When Toni had tried to find out information about Gail Lane, she had had a surprise. What was it?
3 Lenny thought that he was probably involved with Vincent Calab, whether he liked it or not. Why did he think this?

13

1 'Is this a good cheque?' Lenny asked Mike Devine. What did he mean?
2 Who was Mary Sullivan?
3 Who was Mr X?

14

1 Do you think Lenny believed Homer Frank's story about the e-mail threats?
2 Lenny had a bad start in Istanbul. Why was this?
3 'I suggest that you spend the next few hours getting used to your new self,' Julie told Lenny. 'What did she mean?

15

1 Who was Alan Davies?
2 Did Lenny think that Gail would be safe from the blackmailer if she paid for the photos?

3 When Carla shot the scene in the movie which showed Gail and a man escaping from the Topkapi Palace, three different people would be acting the part of the man. Why? Who were they?

16

1 'Wonderful!' Carla said to Lenny and Brent. Why did she say this?
2 'This was definitely not meant to happen!' Lenny shouted to Gail. What did he mean? Where was Gail when Lenny shouted these words?

17

1 Lenny and Gail were being chased and shot at. Lenny decided that the time had come to fight back. What did he do?
2 Lenny was still driving over the bridge, but he couldn't see the Galata Tower any more. Why not?
3 'I didn't know what to say,' Lenny tells the reader. What had he just found out?

18

1 What were Gail's real feelings about Mike Devine?
2 Why was it so important that Senator Democrates never saw the photos of Gail with Vincent Calab?
3 'We're flying,' Lenny told Gail. What had happened?

19

1 Lenny was 'wired for sound'. Why?
2 Why did Brent Foster get a surprise?
3 How did Calab find out that Lenny was not really Brent Foster?

20

1 How did Lenny find out who was blackmailing Gail?
2 Lenny got Gail's money back, but he did not tell the police about the blackmailer. What were his reasons? Do you think Lenny was right?

Glossary

SECTION 1

Terms to do with movies and movie-making

In this story, Lenny has a job working for a movie company. He meets people who act in movies; powerful people who own movie companies; and people who work together while a movie is being made.

blockbuster (page 74)
an extremely popular movie that is successful because many people go to see it.

blue screen (page 30)
a piece of special equipment that is used during the making of a movie. The cameras film the actors in front of a large, bright blue screen. Later, the blue screen part of the film is changed for another piece of film. E.g., if there is a scene where the actors are supposed to be climbing up a tall building, then the second piece of film will be of a tall building. It is easier, cheaper and less dangerous to use a blue screen than to film the scene on a dangerous *location* (See below).

budget (page 27)
the amount of money that a movie-maker has been given to spend on a new movie.

Cameras! Action! (page 48)
the words spoken just before a scene is filmed. It means that the cameras should start filming and the actors must begin to act.

car chase (page 82)
an exciting part of a film where the actors race after each other in cars.

catering trucks (page 47)
vehicles in which food for the crew is prepared and cooked.

chief executive (page 27)
one of the most important and powerful people in a move company.

close-up shot (page 7)
when the camera shows a very close view of the actors as it films a scene.

co-star (page 39)
the other most important actor or actress in a movie.

crane (page 48)
a tall machine with a long arm that can lift heavy things. The camera is put on the *crane* so that the cameraman can get shots from a high position.

crew (page 29)
the many hundreds of people who work together to make a movie.

Cut! (page 48)
the word the director uses to stop the actors and the cameras.

director (page 29)
the person who is in charge of making the movie. The *director* tells the actors what to do and he/she works closely with all the people who help to make the movie. After the movie has been filmed, the director and the *editor* work together to *edit* the film. They cut the film – keeping only the best scenes – and add the *special effects* (See page 120), music etc.

generators (page 47)
machines which make electricity.

hottest actress (in Hollywood) (page 8)
an actress that has just started acting in movies and has suddenly become popular and famous.

lighting cameraman (page 85)
a *technician* (See page 120), who makes sure that the powerful lights that are used are in the correct positions so that the cameras can shoot the scene correctly.

make-up artists (page 48)
the people who can make the movie actors look old, young, hot, cold, beautiful or ugly. *Make-up artists* sometimes use *layers of latex* (page 77) – a special kind of very thin rubber – to give actors' faces a different shape or colour. Make-up artists also use special movie blood to make people look ill or injured.

movie studio (page 24)
a place where a movie company makes movies. The most famous US *studios* are in Hollywood, California. Movie studios are usually a large number of huge buildings on a big piece of land. A *studio* is also the other name for the business organisation or company who makes movies.

movie theatre (page 8)
(Br. Eng. = cinema) the place where people can go and see a movie.

on location (made on location) (page 25)
when all the movie crew and their equipment, the actors and the director go to a different place or country to make part of a film.

plays – *to play* (page 29)
an actor pretends to be a character in the story of the movie. He *plays* or acts a part in a movie.

producer (Ch 2)
the person who gets the money so that a movie can be made.

Producers start with a sum of money from their movie company. Then they ask large companies and rich people to give money for the movie. These companies and people are paid back and also receive extra *profit* when the movie is shown in movie theatres. The producer has to make sure that the director of the movie does not spend more money than is in the *budget*. (See page 118)

rehearse (page 87)
actors *rehearse* when they practise acting together.

schedule (page 51)
the time that is planned to make a film. Because movies are expensive to make, everyone has to keep to a *schedule*. If the movie takes too long, then the costs increase and so profits are less.

set (page 25)
a special place which is built so that a scene can be filmed inside it. The *set* could be a room in a house, a street in a town, or the inside of a ship. All the actors, cameras and crew work inside the set for special scenes in the movie.

shoot scenes (page 25)
film a short part of a movie.

special effects (page 25)
the things which make the people watching the movie believe that it is real. Today, many *special effects* are made on computers. Special effects can show dinosaurs running through forests, spaceships flying in space, bombs exploding, people disappearing and appearing again.

speaking parts (page 25)
the actors who have words to speak in the movie, have *speaking parts*. *Extras* are people who act in films, but do not speak.

studio boss (page 27)
the head of a movie studio.

stunt-double (page 29)
a *stunt* is a dangerous scene in a film. For example, a fight or a car crash are stunts. A *double* is an actor who also looks like the movie star. *Stunt-doubles* are actors who act in these dangerous scenes so that the movie star is not injured. They drive cars in *car chases* (See page 118), and can make them crash.

technicians (page 32)
the people who have special work to do on a movie. *Lighting technicians* look after the lights. *Sound engineers* make sure that the music and the actors' dialogue work together on the movie. Different technicians look after the electricity and the *special effects* (See above).

SECTION 2
Colloquialisms and idioms

Lenny Samuel likes to tell funny stories and make jokes. As he tells this story, he says things which are amusing. Some of the phrases in this section are examples of the expressions that Lenny uses. His words are not always true or serious.

broken up with (someone) (page 65)
stop going out with someone.

can't afford (to stay) (page 72)
have no money to pay for somewhere to stay.

carried away – *got carried away* (page 8)
be so interested in something that you do not think about where you are or what you are doing.

corner of my eye – *out of the corner of my eye* (page 92)
Lenny suddenly sees something at the very edge of where he is looking.

expecting (someone) (page 102)
know that someone is coming to visit you.

fall for (a guy like you) – *I could fall for a guy like you* (page 6)
I might fall in love with you.

fell for it (page 107)
Calab believed Lenny's words and he looked round. He *fell for* Lenny's trick.

head over heels in debt (page 67)
owe large amounts of money to many people.

hell – *what the hell* (page 7)
'I don't care.' This phrase is also a strong way of saying, 'What is happening?'

hit the brakes (page 8)
put your foot down on the brake pedal of a car very quickly and very hard.

hung up (the phone) (page 17)
Mike stops speaking and puts the phone down.

I'm taking a cab (page 12)
I'm going to travel in a taxi.

in shape – *keep myself in shape* (page 6)
done exercises to stay fit, strong and healthy.

involved with (page 17)
had an affair with someone. G*ot involved with the movie industry* (page 68) means someone who does business in the movie industry.

keep an eye on (something) (page 13)
watch what happens to something or to a person.

knocked about (page 65)
be hit many times and be injured while boxing.
line of work – *in my line of work* (page 6)
Lenny is a private detective. It is his *line of work*. He often sees and hears about things like this during his work as a detective.
looks like a million dollars (page 7)
be well dressed and look very attractive.
make yourself comfortable – *to make yourself comfortable* (page 74)
sit and rest for a while.
new man – *to be a new man* (page 22)
Lenny has had a wash, put on clean clothes and had some food. Now he feels bright and full of energy.
not exactly (page 28)
that isn't the whole story.
point – *had a point* (page 6)
Lenny thinks that the woman has said something which is important or true.
put my foot down (page 88)
Lenny put his foot down on the accelerator pedal of the car and made the car go much faster.
see what I can do – *I'll see what I can do* (page 26)
Rik is saying the he will speak to someone in charge and ask if Len can watch part of a movie being made.
shut up (page 90)
Gail is telling Lenny to stop talking and to drive more quickly. This is an impolite way of speaking, but Gail is frightened.
tired of waiting – *to get tired of waiting* (page 42)
leave a place after you have waited for someone for a long time and the person did not arrive.
took charge – *to take charge* (page 32)
Rik told people what to do and where to go.

SECTION 3
American words and expressions

broke (page 70)
have no money at all.
bucks (page 19)
an informal way of talking about US dollars.
cabin (page 24)
a holiday house in the countryside. Cabins are often built on

mountains or near lakes and they are made of wood.

Cool! (page 8)

an informal expression. People use it to mean that someone is confident, good-looking and fashionably dressed. Something which is *cool* is good or interesting.

downtown (page 11)

the southern part of a town. *Uptown* is the northern part of a town. *Downtown* is also sometimes used to mean the poor and unfashionable part of a town, and uptown the rich and fashionable part of a town.

elevator (page 13)

(Br. Eng. = lift) a machine that people use to get from one floor to another in tall buildings.

fella - *Hey, fella, sit down!* (page 7)

a short form of fellow. It is an informal way of saying 'man' or 'mister'.

parking lot (page 8)

(Br. Eng. = car park) an area in a town or city where cars can be left.

real (page 15)

very. *Real mess* (page 15) means that the living-room was very untidy. *Real tight security* (page 25) means that there are many staff to make sure that no one gets into or out of the studios without permission. *Real stunner* (page 6) means that the woman was very beautiful.

sidewalk (page 8)

the path beside the street that people walk on.

SECTION 4
General

amateur (page 6)

someone who does something because they enjoy it. They do not earn any money doing this. An *amateur boxer* (page 6) is someone who fights in boxing matches, but does not earn any money for boxing. *They don't want an American amateur joining in* (page 54) – Lenny is saying that Gail should not dance at the show. She may be able to dance the tango but she will not be as good as the dancers who are paid to do it very well.

barrier (page 92)
a metal bar that comes down across the road to stop traffic going onto the Galata Bridge. When the barrier is down, the traffic stops, then the bridge lifts up and large ships can travel along the Bosphorus.

billion (page 104)
a thousand million.

blackmailed – *to be blackmailed* (page 43)
when someone knows a secret about you and asks you for money. If you will not pay them the money, they will tell everyone your secret.

bleached it and dyed it (page 77)
used chemicals to make dark hair lighter. A dye is then put on the bleached hair to give it a different colour.

bodyguard (page 28)
someone who is paid to look after an important person. Bodyguards are usually strong and good fighters.

business cards (page 13)
small cards which have your name, business address and phone number on them.

cemetery (page 39)
a place where people are buried in graves when they die.

charge – *to charge* (someone) (page 59)
the words that a police officer says when they arrest someone for breaking the law. The person is then taken to a police station and they have to answer questions about what they have done.

contact lenses (page 77)
special pieces of glass or plastic that fit over someone's eyes so that they can see more clearly. Many people wear contact lenses instead of spectacles. Contact lenses can be made in different colours.

crimes – *protection, security, blackmail, corruption, missing persons, small crimes* (page 7)
Lenny has to do many different jobs in his work. Sometimes he protects people from attackers. Sometimes he does *security* work and makes sure that buildings and property are safe. Sometimes he investigates cases of *blackmail* (See above). Sometimes Lenny investigates *corruption*. Corruption is when important people are doing dishonest and illegal things (See also, *clients at the edge of L.A. society*). Sometimes he looks for people who have disappeared – *missing persons*. He also investigates less important crimes – *small crimes*.

deleted – *to delete* (page 75)
remove a piece of information or a message from a computer.

desperate (page 63)
Mike Devine is very frightened as he believes that people are trying to kill him. He is in very bad trouble.

diplomatic licence plates (page 58)
special registration numbers that are on cars belonging to the embassies of foreign countries. The cars are the property of that country and the police cannot arrest the drivers or the passengers.

edges of L.A. society (page 7)
the people who Lenny works for in L.A. – his clients – sometimes break the law. They are not always honest people from the good part of Los Angeles' society.

e-mail (page 28)
an electronic message that can be sent from one computer to another.

fired – *to be fired* (page 62)
be told to leave your job immediately and not be paid.

fists (page 33)
when you close the fingers of your hands tightly together before you fight someone, you are making your hands into *fists*.

handbrake (page 92)
the lever in a car that you pull up when the car has stopped. The handbrake stops the car moving backwards or forwards if you are on a hill.

heavies (page 64)
big, violent men who work for criminals.

intruder (page 17)
a person who enters a building or property without permission.

invested – *to invest in* (someone or something) (page 27)
paid money for someone's work. The movie studios have invested a lot of money in Gail. They hope that they will get more money back when her films become successful.
People *invest* their money in companies. They get their money back in the future. At that time, they will also get some extra money. This extra money is called *the profit*.

Julio – *Avenida 9 de Julio* (page 53)
(**ævenˈiːda ˈnweɪveɪ deɪ ˈhuːliːaʊ**) the widest street in Buenos Aires. It is named for the date – 9th July, 1816 – Argentina's Independence Day.

laundering (page 68)
stolen money or money that has been used in a crime can be recognized by the numbers on the bank notes. So criminals try to spend their illegal money by giving it to companies or businesses. These companies then use this money and they exchange it for

money that has not been used in a crime. This exchange of bad money for good money is known as *laundering*.

life-size (page 49)
the statues have been made the same size as real people.

padding (page 79)
thick pieces of material that are put under clothes to make a person look bigger.

partying– *to party* (page 67)
spending a lot of time and money enjoying yourself – dancing, drinking, eating in expensive restaurants, and perhaps taking drugs.

pier (page 91)
a wall or piece of land beside the sea where people can get on or off ships.

playboy (page 67)
a very rich man who does not need to work. He spends a great amount of money on travelling, cars, food, drink, gambling and beautiful women.

private eye (page 13)
this is a word joke. Lenny is a private detective, or a private investigator – a P.I. Often, his work is to look for missing people, things or money. The 'I' in P.I. sounds like 'eye'. Lenny uses his eyes and watches what people do. The expression, *keep an eye on something*, means to watch something carefully.

rarely (page 6)
does not happen often.

represented – *to represent* (page 71)
working for someone and speaking for them in meetings.

risk – *to take a risk* (page 28)
do something, although you know that it is dangerous.

rotors (page 99)
very long, thin pieces of metal on the roof of a helicopter. *Rotors* turn round very quickly and pull the helicopter into the air.

ruthless (page 44)
very tough and dangerous person.

running (page 88)
the engine of the Mercedes was switched on, but the car was not moving forwards.

ruthlessness– *reputation for ruthlessness* (page 67)
people know that Democrates is a tough and powerful man. He will do anything to succeed in his plans.

scandal (page 97)
when a person behaves badly or does something wrong and other people find out about it – this is a *scandal*. Scandals about famous

people are often reported in newspapers.

security pass (page 25)
a badge showing your name and details. A *security pass* can be checked to see if you can work in the place you are going to.

senator – *US senator* (page 67)
an American politician who speaks for the people of his/her city or state to the central government in Washington D.C. Senators are chosen by the people of their city or state – they are *elected*.

siren (page 56)
a machine that makes a loud noise to warn of danger. A *siren* on a police car warns people that the police car is coming along very fast.

skidded – *to skid* (page 92)
the car moved sideways when it tried to stop suddenly.

statements – *taking statements* (page 37)
police officers *take statements* when they listen to people's stories about a crime, or an accident, and write them down.

stunner (page 6)
a very good-looking man or woman. This person is described as *stunning*. Everyone is amazed how beautiful that person is.

suspicious (page 38)
something that is wrong, strange or unusual.

swerved – *to swerve* (page 88)
moved very quickly around another vehicle on the road.

tombs (page 48)
buildings where dead people are buried (See *cemetery* on page 124). *Tombs* are often made of expensive stone and have carved statues on them.

tramlines (page 87)
trams are buses that move along metal tracks in city streets. Trams are powered by electricity. The metal tracks are called *tramlines*.

transmit – *to transmit* (page 102)
the microphone will send a message to the tape recorder. The tape recorder will record the conversations that Lenny hears.

Exercises

Background

Read about Lenny, then tick the best answers below.

> I'm a private investigator – that is, a private detective – in Los Angeles, California. My clients are often people who live on the edges of L.A. society. Protection, security, blackmail, corruption, missing persons, small crimes - these are the things I deal with every day. Sometimes, I even have a murder case. The only jobs I don't do are divorce cases and marriage problems.
>
> My life isn't easy, but there is usually enough money each month to pay the rent for my apartment and the rent for my office.

1 Why do some people use a private detective instead of the police?
- a ☐ Because private detectives are more friendly.
- b ☐ Because private detectives are cheaper.
- c ☑ Because they don't want to get involved with the police.
- d ☐ Because the police do not handle small crimes.

2 What do you understand by *people who live on the edges of society*?
- a ☐ Rich people who are above the law.
- b ☐ People who are not respectable.
- c ☐ Law-abiding citizens.
- d ☐ People who work in Hollywood.

3 What does *protection* and *security* work involve?
- a ☐ Guarding someone or something.
- b ☐ Being a spy.
- c ☐ Selling things.
- d ☐ Working for a bank.

4 What is *blackmail*?

a ☐ Selling things illegally.

b ☐ Stealing things from letters.

c ☐ Sending advertisements to people who do not want them.

d ☐ Threatening to reveal bad information about people unless they pay money.

5 Do clients expect Lenny Samuel to blackmail people for them?

a ☐ Yes, if they pay him enough.

b ☐ Yes, because all divorce cases and marriage problems involve blackmail.

c ☐ No, they expect him to find blackmailers.

d ☐ No, Lenny does not take divorce cases.

6 What is *corruption*?

a ☐ Dishonest or illegal behaviour by officials.

b ☐ Crimes in the meat-packaging industry.

c ☐ Grave-robbing.

d ☐ Tapping of telephones.

7 What *missing person* cases can a private investigator handle better than the police?

a ☐ Cases where no crime is involved.

b ☐ Cases where the missing person is very rich.

c ☐ Kidnapping and ransom cases.

d ☐ Cases where the missing person has run away with money.

8 Which of the following are *small crimes*?

a ☐ Murder.

b ☐ Kidnapping.

c ☐ Bank robbery.

d ☐ Petty theft.

9 How much money does Lenny make?

a ☐ A lot, because he works in Hollywood.

b ☐ Enough to pay the rent.

c ☐ He has a regular salary.

d ☐ His income is more than adequate.

Grammar Focus 1: *as if*

At the cinema, Lenny finds himself looking at a woman who 'dresses as if she had a million dollars'.

We often use the past tense after *as if* to show that we are making an 'unreal' comparison. Lenny doesn't know whether the woman does have a million dollars, but she dresses like someone who does.

Rewrite the sentences using *as if* and the past tense.

1 I've never met him before, but he speaks to me like we're old friends.
I've never met him before, but he speaks to me as if we were old friends.

2 He doesn't have much money, but he acts like a millionaire.

....

....

3 My aunt is staying with me at the moment. She treats me like her own daughter.

....

....

4 He doesn't know much about photography, but he talks like an expert.

....

....

5 She wears thick jumpers and heavy coats all the time. I think she thinks it's winter.

....

....

6 He works really slowly. I think he thinks we have all the time in the world.

....

....

Writing

Look at Lenny's notes. Write about his first meeting with Gail Lane and Mike Devine, adding as much extra detail as possible.

1 road accident near Purple Palace
2 white car hit Chrysler - me fine, my car OK - other car badly smashed
3 driver - Mike Devine - blood on face, very angry; drunk - collapsed
4 passenger - Gail Lane - v calm, apologetic
5 took Devine home - doorman helped me - carried Devine to elevator - up to apartment - found his keys
6 apartment wrecked - clothes and books on floor - windows open
7 put him in shower - then someone hit me

1	*One night I had a road accident near the Purple Palace nightclub in Los Angeles.*
2	
3	
4	
5	
6	
7	

At Mike Devine's Apartment

Complete the gaps. Use each word in the box once.

owe ~~police~~ succeeded street warning hit garage frighten underneath elevator apartment doorman wrecked rang wouldn't

'My car's outside,' I said. 'The [1]..........*police*.......... will take it away if I leave it in the [2]...................................... any longer.'

'Put the car in the [3]......................................,' Mike said. 'There's a garage [4].. the apartment building, and the [5]...................................... goes straight down to it.'

'So, someone could have left the [6].., then taken the elevator down to the garage and driven away without the [7].. seeing them,' I said.

At that moment the phone [8]...................................... . Mike Devine answered it. 'Yes,' he said. 'Yes, I see.' Then he hung up. He looked terrible.

'Who was it?' I asked.

'Someone I [9].............................. some money to,' he replied. 'He said that he [10]... the apartment. He said it was a [11].. . He said he was sorry he had [12].............................. you. He thought you were me! And he said that next time he [13]... wreck my apartment – he would wreck *me*!'

So the person who had hit me on the head was trying to [14].. Mike Devine. And he had [15].. . Mike was looking very frightened indeed.

Grammar Focus 2: Reported Speech

When we use reported speech, we don't usually use the same tense as the original speaker. We go one tense further back into the past. We also change the time expressions we use.

For example:
this afternoon > that afternoon
today > that day
tomorrow > the next day
now > then / at that moment / at that time

Rewrite the statements below in reported speech.

1 'Mike Devine is drunk tonight.'
Gail said (that) Mike Devine was drunk that night.

2 'I didn't hit Lenny on the head this evening.'
He said (that) ....

....

3 'Gail Lane is making a new movie now.'
They said (that) ....

4 'I've received threatening letters this week.'
She said (that) ....

....

5 'Josie broke both her legs today.'
He said (that) ....

6 'Gail has gone out on her own this evening.'
They said (that) ....

....

7 'We have been keeping an eye on Gail this week.'
Captain Garcia said (that) ....

....

8 'Gail is in great danger at this time.'
Lenny said (that) ....

Words From the Story

C	P	S	S	E	C	R	R	X	T
S	R	I	C	I	T	A	M	R	T
E	O	D	B	A	R	R	M	T	C
N	D	E	O	U	N	E	A	P	B
A	U	W	H	B	D	D	N	M	U
T	C	A	S	I	R	G	A	D	C
O	E	L	S	U	B	O	E	L	K
R	R	K	S	K	I	D	K	T	S
X	B	A	R	R	I	E	R	E	B
D	O	W	N	T	O	W	N	E	I

Find words in the square with the meanings below. The numbers in brackets show the number of letters in each word.

1 a traffic obstacle (7) ......*BARRIER*......
2 slang: having little or no money at present (5) ....
3 slang: dollars (5) ....
4 the amount of money available for making or producing something (6) ....
5 the centre of a town (8) ....
6 the man responsible for financing a movie (8) ....
7 a shocking situation usually involving important people (7) ....
8 a member of the US Senate (7) ....
9 pavement (US) (8) ....
10 a device that makes a loud noise (5)
11 to slide across the ground (4) ....
12 a town bus which runs on tracks (4) ....

Multiple Choice

Tick the best answer.

1 What did Rik and Lenny have in common?
a ☐ They both used to work for the police, and they were both from immigrant families.
b ☐ Their families both came from Puerto Rico.
c ☐ Rik had also worked as a private detective.
d ☐ They both used to work for the police, and they were both Italian-Americans.

2 What was Gail doing in the Café Pernambuco in Buenos Aires?
a ☐ She was waiting to meet Theo Democrates.
b ☐ She had arranged to meet Lenny.
c ☐ She had been told to go there by someone who was blackmailing her.
d ☐ She had arranged to meet Vincent Calab.

3 Who tried to drop a stone ball on Gail Lane at the Recoleta Cemetery in Buenos Aires?
a ☐ Rik Roma.
b ☐ Vincent Calab's men.
c ☐ Theo Democrates' men.
d ☐ Annie and Arabella.

4 Miss Sullivan told Mike Devine to leave LA and never to see Gail Lane again. Who was she working for?
a ☐ Vincent Calab.
b ☐ Rik Roma.
c ☐ Homer Frank.
d ☐ Theo Democrates.

5 Why was Vincent Calab trying to kill Gail Lane?
a ☐ He was threatening Homer Frank, who owed him a lot of money.
b ☐ He was working for Theo Democrates, who was very jealous.
c ☐ He was working for Rik Roma, who was blackmailing Gail.
d ☐ He was working for Mike Devine, who had borrowed a lot of money from Gail.

Published by Macmillan Heinemann ELT
Between Towns Road, Oxford OX4 3PP
Macmillan Heinemann ELT is an imprint of
Macmillan Publishers Limited
Companies and representatives throughout the world
Heinemann is a registered trademark of Pearson Education, used under licenece.

ISBN 978-0-230-03055-8
ISBN 978-1-4050-7711-8 (with CD pack)

First published 1999

This edition first published 2005

Illustrated by Peter Richardson
Original cover template design by Jackie Hill
Cover illustration by Mark Oldroyd

Printed in Thailand
2014 2013 2012

15 14 13 12 11

without CD pack
2013 2012 2011

8 7 6 5 4